PENALISED

SUPPRESSION – THE BATTLE FOR EMANCIPATION
IN 19TH CENTURY IRELAND
OR
THE HEDGE TEACHERS OF TIPPERARY

The struggle for survival by one family

The Prequel to FIRST TO GO

By

Pam Skelton

*Dedicated to the ancestors and descendants of the Frisby family
from Islands, near Ballingarry and Mullinahone,
County Tipperary, Ireland.*

FAMILY TREE OF

THE FRISBY FAMILY OF ISLANDS

Generation One

Richard Frisby (a cooper by trade) m. Eleanor Whelan

Lived in Carrick-on-Suir

John, Thomas, Patrick, three daughters and two more sons

Generation Two

John Frisby (a cooper by trade) m. Catherine

Moved to Islands, near Ballingarry, County Tipperary

Richard (hedge teacher) plus several brothers and sisters

Generation Three

Richard Frisby (hedge teacher) m. Mary Walsh

Catherine (Kate) 1815

John (Jack, farmer)1817

Richard (Dick – hedge teacher)1820

Thomas (Tom)1822

Michael (Mikey)1830

Generation Four

John (Jack) Frisby (farmer) m. Catherine Ryan

Richard 1838 (national school teacher)

Catherine 1842

Bridget 1844

John 1848

Margaret 1851

Generation Five

Richard Frisby (national school teacher) m. Mary Corcoran

Catherine 1875

Margaret 1877

Bridget 1878

John 1880

Thomas 1883

Patrick 1885

Richard 1886

Mary Ann 1888

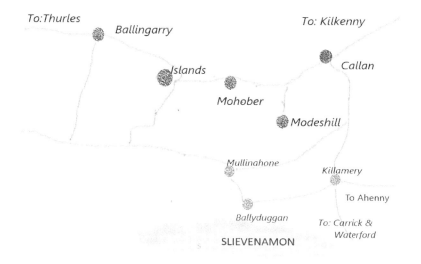

SKETCH MAP OF PART OF SOUTHERN TIPPERARY
SHOWING ISLANDS AND ITS RELATIONSHIP TO
BALLINGARRY AND MULLINAHONE

CHARACTERS IN THE BOOK

CARRICK-ON-SUIR
Thomas Frisby
Eleanora Frisby
Matty Connell, the tack man

ISLANDS
The Frisby family – generations 1 to 5 on family tree
Thomas Frisby and his wife Nellie, their son George Frisby and his wife Mary Marnell

THE WALSH FAMILY
Mr and Mrs Walsh
Mary Walsh
Martin Walsh

MODESHILL
The Ryan family

BALLYDUGGAN
Thomas Frisby
David Frisby and Catherine Tyrell and their children

KILLAMERY
The Killamery Frisby family

AHENNY
Thomas Frisby

"REDACRES", MULLINAVAT, SOUTHERN KILKENNY

James Frisby
Michael Frisby, Johanna and family

CASUAL VISITORS TO ISLANDS

Sean the tinker
Joan the handywoman and her daughter Margaret
Patrick the bonesetter

VARIOUS TEACHERS

Joe Cooney near Islands
Tom Cahill and his brother William at Thurles
Edmund Rice at Waterford

BALLINGARRY

The parish priest, Father O'Brien

PROMINENT NATIONAL FIGURES

Daniel O'Connell, Leader of the Catholic Association
William Smith O'Brien, Leader of Young Ireland
Thomas Francis Meagher
Richard O'Gorman

Education is the passport to the future, for tomorrow belongs to those who prepare for it today.

Malcolm X

You cannot conquer Ireland. You cannot extinguish the Irish passion for freedom. If our deed has not been sufficient to win freedom, then our children will win by a better deed.

Patrick Henry Pearse (Irish teacher)

PREFACE

This is the story of the Frisby family from Islands, Ballingarry, County Tipperary, Ireland. The story covers a time span of over 100 years from the late 18th century through to the end of the 19th century. It is a prequel to *First to Go*, which tells the true story of Bridget Frisby.

The story tells the tale of Bridget's ancestors. This short preface before you read the book will help you understand the difficulties the family encountered over the years.

¤

In days gone by, the whole of Ireland was part of the British Empire. In the mid-seventeenth century, before and after Cromwell had brutally raided Ireland, the British were constantly trying to bring Ireland under their control. Cromwell and his army wreaked havoc in the country, and as they progressed through the land, they left in their wake ruined, burnt-out homes and desecrated churches. They killed many people.

The majority of native Irish were Catholics but the British Government wanted to impose the Anglican religion on the Irish, as they had tried to do in England. In 1695, the British government introduced the Penal Laws for Ireland which sought to curb the Catholic religion on the island.

Under the Penal Laws, Irish Catholics were not allowed to follow their religion. Those churches which had escaped ruin by Cromwell were banned. In 1696, all Catholic bishops were banished from the country. As a result of these draconian laws, Catholics were hampered in their everyday life. They were not allowed to serve in public office; inter-marrying was not allowed; they could not own firearms; they were not allowed to vote; they could not own or inherit land; it was illegal to worship as a Catholic and, worst of all, they were not allowed an education.

Ireland was a strong resilient nation and the Irish had deep religious beliefs which they refused to give up. This strength helped them to find other ways of practising their religion and educating their children. They set about evading the law in every way possible. Those priests who remained held mass in the fields, out of sight of the law. People crowded round the Mass Rock to receive the supplement. These Mass Rocks can still be seen in Ireland today.

A few educated Catholics set themselves up as teachers. They taught their pupils in the fields, often under shelter and hidden by the hedges. These schools were aptly named hedge schools, run by teachers of the hedge. As time progressed, many of these hedge schools moved indoors, into old barns or mud huts. Some parents paid a small fee for their children's education. Those who had no money paid in kind with items of food or clothing. Some gave the teacher a roof over his head in lieu of fees. So, basic education continued in Ireland in those terrible years. Lessons in reading, writing and arithmetic were provided, and even, in some instances, Latin and Greek. Latin was the language of the Catholic church and many teachers had studied it in the years before the Penal Laws. The teachers were eager to pass their knowledge on to the children, and most parents wanted their children to receive it.

Priests and teachers were outlawed by the state but often worked together to illegally set up the facilities required to achieve their joint aims: worship and education.

We find the Frisby family in this restricted atmosphere in Ireland – seeking to find a better life for their family and, most of all, to educate their children and to follow their religion.

Most of the characters in this book are genuine and actually lived through these troubled times. However, one or two extra people have been added for the sake of the story. Most of the events are factually correct, though they have been embellished in parts.

PART ONE

CHAPTER ONE

It's 1785 and we are in a smoky bar in a tiny pub in County Tipperary, Ireland. It's one of the many pubs in Carrick-on-Suir. It's a Friday night. The men are sitting with their mugs of porter and the usual gossip abounds. Smoke fills the air. They're relaxing after a hard week's work.

They all have their pay packets in their pockets but only a few will go home with their pay intact. Friday night is drinking night. The men have worked hard all week and they believe it's their right to spend their pay in the pub on Fridays. The same scene is being re-enacted in all the other pubs throughout the town, and indeed throughout Ireland, where thirsty workers meet their mates for Friday drinks after work. It's a ritual not to be missed.

Suddenly, one of the men notices one of their regulars, John Frisby, isn't with them.

"Sure," asked Paddy O'Brien, "where's John tonight? He's usually the first to arrive and he's not here. What can be wrong, I wonder?"

"Perhaps his mother caught him on the way home," said one of the men.

They all laughed.

"Maybe he's working overtime," said another.

"No, it can't be that, there isn't enough work. The bosses are too mean to pay overtime."

"I reckon there's something wrong. We'll find out sooner or later."

"Perhaps one of us should go and knock on his door."

"Well, I'm not going anywhere till I've had my pint," said Tom Larkin.

They all agreed.

The muffled conversation continued. Suddenly, half an hour later, there was a bang at the door and it swung open. Who should appear but John Frisby!

"Heh! Come in!" they all cried.

"Where've you been? What's kept you?"

John was panting. He'd been running to get there. "Sure, I'm late for my pint," he said, "but I've got some good news."

"What's that?" they all said.

"I've got myself a regular job."

"Begorra, where?" they all chorused.

"Sure, it's at my father's place. You know. Where they do the coopering. When I was a boy, my father wouldn't take me on. He said I was a lazy so and so. Now he's begging me to work for him. Anyway, I start on Monday. I don't know what I'll be doing but surely there's plenty to learn and I can progress. 'Twill be good for me. The regular money will be better than the intermittent pay I get from the odd jobs I do now."

They all applauded him and a cheer went up. Everyone wanted a secure job. But these were few and far between. John was popular with the men and no one begrudged him his good luck. Most of the men helped out on farms but work was irregular and so was their pay. Times like today, when they had all been working, were good ones. The ups and downs of life were hard.

¤

John joined his father in his cooperage business. He knew nothing about coopering but he was eager to learn. To start with his father kept him on a tight rein and didn't let him make any barrels. For the first six months he was the general dog's body. He ran here and there on errands. He took the finished barrels down to the river to be shipped to Waterford where they would be sold. He swept the workroom floor and collected the willow branches from the pond where they had been soaking. These were used by the women in the basket making side of the business. He was never idle. As he worked, he watched his father working on the barrels and began to understand how they were made. He hoped it would not be long before his father started his training. It was a long wait and he wondered if he had made the right move, but the regular wage was not to be sniffed at.

Six months later his father took him to one side.

"John, I want you to learn coopering. We'll start today."

John never looked back. He was born to do the job. His hands crafted the wood even better than his father; he was a natural.

John was the youngest son in the family. He had three elder brothers who had gone abroad to Newfoundland and to America.

The brothers had ventured overseas because there wasn't enough work for them in the family business. There was no future for them in Ireland. John and his brother Thomas were the only ones left at home. They had sisters but they were all married and lived away. Thomas also worked in the family business, but he was a slower worker than John and didn't get involved with the barrel making. As time progressed, John was making his own barrels and Thomas was his assistant. John loved his work and each barrel was crafted with care. His father was proud of him.

A year after John started working for his father, he met a young girl at church called Catherine. They became good friends and often walked out together. John had never had a girlfriend before. At first, it was strange walking out with Catherine and holding her hand. His friends had always been his mates in the pub, a place never frequented by women. After a few months he realised how much he liked her and wondered if she was the girl for him. John worried about where they would live if he asked her to marry him.

One day, John was sitting in the kitchen with his mother and, taking advantage of the absence of his father, he said, "Ma, if I got married, could I still live here with my wife?" His question was greeted with silence as his mother thought about how they would manage. John went over to her and put his arm around her shoulder. "Ma, you don't have to answer straight away. I was just wondering."

His mother laughed.

"Don't I know you only too well, John? You wouldn't be asking me unless you had a young lass in mind. Do I know her?"

"Aw, give over, Mam. I was just wondering."

"You can't pull the wool over my eyes, John. Haven't I noticed you taking longer to wash yourself in the mornings and taking more care of yourself. Am I right? Are you hankering after a young lassie?"

John confessed he had been seeing a girl.

"I thought so. Is it anyone I know?"

"You might know her from church, Mam. Her name is Catherine Mason. Her father runs the corner shop on the next road. We've been walking out for a little while now. Mam, I love her and I want to ask her to marry me but we have nowhere to live."

"That's good news. I know the Masons. They're a good family. But I can't see how you can bring her here to live. As you know, your father and I sleep in the big bedroom and the only other space is the little room where you and Thomas sleep. I don't think we would manage. But let me think on it."

John was disappointed at his mother's reply but understood the problem. He realised he would have to find another lodging if they were to marry.

"Don't tell anyone, Mam, please. I haven't asked her yet and she might refuse me."

"Don't worry. I can keep a secret. But don't be leaving it too long now or someone else will snap her up. A nice girl like her won't wait around long, particularly if another handsome lad comes her way!"

John was dismayed. It looked as if he would have to move out of the family home. The next time he saw his brother Thomas, he said to him, "I heard a rumour you're moving out of the house. Any truth in that?" Thomas looked surprised and didn't answer straight away.

"Who told you that?" he said to John. "I haven't told Ma and Pa yet. Who's been spreading tales?"

"Oh, so it's true, is it? Who's the lucky lass?"

Thomas asked John to keep it to himself but said he was hoping to marry his girlfriend, Nellie.

"Well," said John, "you'd better get your skates on before someone else snaps her up. All the lads like her. Nice girls like her are quickly snapped up. Where will you both live?"

Thomas said he was hoping they could move in with Nellie's family, who had a spare room. He knew Nellie didn't want to leave home. John chuckled to himself; he hadn't heard a rumour, but his pretence had paid off.

John realised Thomas would soon be moving out. The small room where he and Thomas slept would soon be free for him and Catherine. He decided there and then to ask Catherine to marry him.

Catherine was fond of John and was delighted. She was quick to say "Yes" when he popped the question.

"Where will we live?" she immediately asked.

"Thomas will soon be moving out and a room will be free in our house," John told her, asking her to keep it secret.

They decided to wait until the room was free before getting married.

"I hope it won't be long," said Catherine.

The next Sunday, John and Catherine announced to John's family that they were engaged to be married. Thomas was very surprised to hear this news.

"You old fox!" he said to John. "You didn't tell me this the other day. You've raced me to it."

John laughed and said, "I told you. Nice girls don't wait for long. You have to act quickly or you will lose them!"

Thomas nodded. "Err, yes, I suppose you're right. Perhaps I should hurry up and ask Nellie."

And so, John, Catherine, Thomas and Nellie were all married on the same day.

It was a traditional Irish wedding with all the families present and a large party afterwards. Relatives came from far and wide to celebrate. News always travelled fast in Ireland and one of the visitors to the wedding was Thomas Frisby, their uncle, who came from further north in County Tipperary. He lived at the foot of Slievenamon where he had his own farm. John and his uncle Thomas struck up a firm friendship.

After their wedding, John and Catherine went to stay with Uncle Thomas for a few days. During the evenings, their talks covered a wide range of subjects from families to farming and politics. One day, Thomas asked John if he was happy working for his father. John said he loved the work but he worried his pay wasn't enough to support him and Catherine. It would be even worse when they had children. He told Thomas he'd asked his father for a pay rise. But his father had said, "I'm sorry, son, but there's no more money in the pot." John thought his father was a bit mean. The worry was making him unhappy. Thomas asked John if he was confident enough to start his own cooperage business. John said he'd thought about it but his father had monopolised the business in Carrick so there was no chance of running a business there.

Before Catherine and John returned home, Thomas took John to one side.

"I understand your problem but you know there *is* a solution. Why don't you move up here to the Mullinahone area? There is no competition here and the area is ideal for your business. The raw materials for your trade – wood and water – are plentiful. All the local farmers would become your customers and you can also sell your barrels at the markets. You would have a choice of three markets: Mullinahone, Ballingarry and Callan. There are shops in nearby Callan if you need to buy items for your business. You can also shop in Kilkenny town which is not too far away. There would be no opposition to setting up a cooperage business in this vicinity. In fact, it would be welcomed."

John thanked Thomas for his advice and said he would think about it.

On the way home, John told Catherine about his uncle's suggestion. Catherine was full of enthusiasm for it.

"Hold on now," said John. "Not too fast. We need to think this through thoroughly. There's a lot involved."

No more was said about the proposition and life continued as before. One year after their wedding, John and Catherine had their first child. It was a boy and they called him Richard after his grandfather. John's parents were delighted with their first grandchild.

Now there was an extra mouth to feed and John worried even more about his earnings.

"You know," he said to Catherine. "I'm thinking about Uncle Thomas's suggestion of moving near him and starting my own business. We won't have any customers to start with so things will be difficult. We'll have to sell our first barrels at market. I'm sure we'll be successful and, before long, the farmers will get to know us. When they need more barrels, they will come to us directly. I know that eventually we'll be better off if we do this. The more I think about it, I'd love to run my own business. We must look into it again."

John wrote to Thomas telling him he was considering moving near Mullinahone and starting a business. He asked Thomas if he knew of any suitable places where they could live and run a business. He heard nothing for a few weeks. One day a letter arrived from Thomas. He said that he had been looking around for a while and a house had just come available in the townland of Islands, which was just three miles outside Mullinahone. He said the house was suitable for many purposes and several people were interested in it, so time was of the essence. He urged John to visit as soon as possible.

Things moved very quickly after that. John went to look at the property in Islands and was delighted with it. It was a thatched house with a kitchen and a parlour downstairs and two big bedrooms upstairs. It was ideal for them. It was plenty big enough for them even if they had more children. There were two acres of land attached to the house which were suitable for farming. The bonus was an outbuilding which would be suitable as a cooper's workshop.

John knew it would be difficult to find another dwelling which came with a workshop.

Islands was a strange name for the townland and John wondered where the name originated. When he visited the house, he spoke with the locals. An elderly man who had lived there all his life told him why the area was called Islands. He pointed out the little river which ran at the front of the house.

"In days gone by, there was a river at the back of the house as well, just two fields away. So, this parcel of land was like an island between the rivers. But the river at the back dried up years ago and can no longer be seen. That's where the name came from but it sounds strange today."

In fact, Islands was just a small, remote Irish hamlet with less than six houses.

After looking over the house, the outbuildings and the land, John met with the landlord's agent. After a few outstanding questions had been answered to his satisfaction, he was quick to sign the new lease. John now had the unenviable task of telling his father he would be moving away to start his own business. He didn't look forward to this, but it had to be done.

When he heard the news, John's father was irate.

"Who will take your place when you are gone? Good workmen don't grow on trees. Men with coopering skills are few and far between. It'll take me two or three years to find someone to replace you."

John stood there and listened to his father.

"Father, if you had paid me a decent wage, I wouldn't have taken this step. The fault lies at your door, not mine." John turned and walked out of the door.

It was not long before John and Catherine had gathered together their few belongings. Within a week of announcing to his father they were leaving, John and Catherine set out for their new life at Islands. John was sad to leave the family home. Just as they were about to go, John's father appeared, breathless, outside the back door.

"Oh good," he said. "I'm glad I caught you before you left. I've put one or two things together for you. Come and have a look." John stepped outside and was amazed at his father's generosity. There was a small sack of flour, another of oats and finally one which contained seed potatoes.

"Thanks, Pa," John said as he hugged his father. "That'll tide us over until we are settled. Thank you so much."

Most of all John hated saying goodbye to his mother who stood on their cottage doorstep as they left with tears in her eyes.

"Come and visit us soon. Good luck for the future!" she said. She waved to them as they made their way up the road. John wondered when he would see his parents again.

As John and Catherine turned the corner in the road, they bumped into John's brother Thomas.

"I'm sorry you're going but I wish you luck. But you've left me in a mess – I'll have to cope with the old man's mood now. Keep in touch with us."

John regretted leaving Thomas and realised he would be in a difficult position.

"Aye, we will, Thomas," he said as he waved goodbye. "We'll write to you and let you know how we're faring."

CHAPTER TWO

It was 1788 when John and Catherine left Carrick with their young son, Richard, and made their move to Islands. On their way to their new home, John said, "Catherine, I know I've said this before but I hope you realise hard times lie ahead. We have little money behind us and no customers. From here on it'll be an uphill struggle."

Catherine put her arm around him and said, "Don't worry John, we'll manage. We'll have a roof over our heads which is more than some people have. As soon as people realise what a good cooper you are, they'll be queuing up at the door for your goods. I have every faith in you and we'll weather the storm together."

¤

John and Catherine had both been born in Carrick. Neither of them had travelled far before their move to Islands. They saw many changes in their lives when they made the move. At first, John struggled to set up his business but after two years it was flourishing. He was making beer kegs, firkins and butter churns. A side-line to his business was basket making. The baskets were made from willow saplings and Catherine helped him with the weaving. Baskets had many uses on farms and they sold these with the barrels at local fairs.

In the next few years, Catherine had two more babies and they became a family of five. John was glad they'd made the move to Islands.

"We would never have managed to feed all the family on the meagre wage I was getting from father," he said to Catherine one night. They agreed the move was the best thing they could have done.

Just opposite their new home was a fast-flowing stream which eventually joined the King's River about half a mile away. The stream provided a plentiful supply of water for domestic needs and it was ideal for treating the willow saplings which were used in basket making. Drinking water came from the pump just down the lane. The area around Islands was mostly flat land. In summer, it was verdant. The fields were interspersed with small woods. Peat bogs were few and far apart in the district but, at the lower end of their land, there was a small bog which supplied them with turf for their fire. Although the land was flat, in the distance they could see Slievenamon in all its beauty. Depending on the weather, the colour of the mountain changed from green to blue to purple. It was a magnificent sight

A few years after their move, John's cooperage was very well established in the area. John was pleased. He was now receiving orders from local farmers and was still selling barrels at the local market in Callan. John was glad they had made the move.

Catherine had settled well at Islands and loved the house. She came from a large family and she told John she never missed her brothers and sisters who were always quarrelling. It was very quiet at Islands, apart from the sound of their young children. She soon set about putting her mark on the house and making it as comfortable as possible. She was a great support to John in their first few difficult years. She knew he was a good craftsman and all would come well in due course. It was unusual for a young family to have such a nice house and the land was a bonus. The kitchen soon became the hub of the home and whenever John came in from the workshop, there was always a meal waiting for him.

"To be sure I smelt the stew as I walked up the path and I knew I was in for a good supper!" he'd say.

Their young son, Richard, was growing up fast. He was no longer the only child and he enjoyed the company of his younger siblings, another boy and a girl. The children kept Catherine busy and she had never been happier. During the summer, the children played happily out in the fields, often joined by their neighbours' children.

¤

In March 1792, John and Catherine Frisby sat by the fire in the kitchen, huddled together to keep warm. The children were all in bed. It was the first time that day John and Catherine had had time to talk together. It was always bedlam in their small house until the children were safely tucked up in bed. Their eldest son, Richard, was five years old now and John was keen for him to have some sort of education. It was against the law for them, under the Penal Laws, to educate their children but like all parents, they wanted the best for him. This was the first time in their marriage they had been unable to solve a problem.

"We've achieved so much since we came here," John said, "and been through much hardship together. But now we're having difficulty with such a simple thing. We've no idea where the schools are in this area – if indeed there *are* any. All we want to do is to send our son to school. It's proving more difficult than everything we've done."

As they warmed themselves by the fire, John turned to his wife.

"As you know, Cath, I can read a little and I have knowledge of my numbers. I wouldn't be able to carry on my business without that. I only trade in a small way and the coopering accounts form most of our income. Since we started making baskets, life has been a little easier. I'm glad we have the farm as a standby but as I spend most of my time in the workshop, I have little time to look after it. I hope in years to come our sons will take to the land. We are just getting by and times are still hard. I see a future where we have a large family and our sons will run the farm. Farming will bring extra income and in future we'll be comfortable. I see good days ahead. But now, with so many mouths to feed, it gets harder every year. Young Richard is five now and he's a bright little chap. I know he'll benefit from learning even though it's going to be difficult to afford it."

"I agree we must do the best for him, but how? With the law as it is, how did you come to learn your letters and numbers?" asked Catherine, who had never been to school herself.

"When we were in Carrick, we had a hedge teacher called Mick O'Donnell. He was a grand chap and all the children loved him. He taught us in an old mud hut by the River Suir, out of the way of prying eyes. At one time there were eleven of us. We all had to come and go at different times so as not to attract attention or arouse suspicion. Mick was a wanderer with nowhere of his own to live so he stayed at one of the boy's houses. Parents who couldn't afford to pay school fees gave him a roof over his head and food in his stomach. Some parents paid him in kind with eggs, apples or milk. Most of the parents were farming folk and didn't have much money. People scrimped and scraped to be able to send their children to him. One time he stayed with us but he didn't stay long. He slept on the floor in our little kitchen. Our little abode was too cramped for him. I learnt enough in his small school to see me through life and I'm forever grateful to him. But, with a better education I could have done so much more. I want the best for Richard and in time for all our children."

Catherine moved towards the fire and lifted the large black pot from the fire and made their usual evening drink. She poured the gently warmed milk into their mugs. This time of evening was always the best part of the day, when the children were in bed and they had time to themselves to relax and talk together.

"Why are these schools called hedge schools? I've always wondered," Cath mused.

"Oh, well, it's to do with the Penal Laws. As we are Catholic, we're not allowed to educate our children. When the Penal Laws first came in, teachers taught the children in the fields, hidden by a hedge, away from prying eyes, as far away from the interfering arm of the law as possible. They always chose a field with a very thick hedge which would block them from the view of passersby. So, they were called hedge schools. Some teachers posted a look-out at the entrance to the field to warn of anyone approaching. It was all very secretive. Times have changed and now these unofficial teachers find somewhere indoors to teach, like a barn or an empty cabin. It's better now that they have shelter but even so we still call them hedge schools. They are still illegal. Life is so difficult. I don't think the English will ever repeal the laws."

"Now we're living near Mullinahone, surely there will be some form of education available? Have you asked around?"

"Not yet, Cath, but that's my next job. Richard is growing up fast so we can't leave it much longer. We'll have to find a way to pay the teacher but I'm sure we'll manage. As you know, the Catholic priests and the teachers are all forbidden by law to follow their professions. As a result, they stick together. I'll speak to the priest. I'm sure he'll be able to point me in the right direction!"

¤

The draconian Penal Laws had been concocted by the British government in London and their purpose was to keep the Catholics in Ireland down. There were so many restrictions. Religion and education were barred but the law forbade them in many other ways too. The poor Catholic Irish men and women were suppressed and, in those days, it was almost a sin to be a Catholic.

But the Catholics were not easily beaten down. Their fighting spirit helped them to overcome these difficulties. It led to Mass being said in the fields and their children being taught in the fields. They were determined that a 'foreign' government wouldn't impede their progress. Even though they were part of Britain, they looked on the British as foreigners. The Irish wanted to be free of the British so they could rule their own country.

A few days later, John met the priest and talked to him about education for Richard. The priest gave him the names of three hedge teachers operating locally. He decided to visit all three of them in their 'schools' and he would choose the one he thought best for Richard.

CHAPTER THREE

I knew Da was looking for a teacher for me but I was sworn to secrecy. Da told me not to tell my brother and sister. He explained to me that schools were illegal and he didn't want me talking about it until plans had been finalised. He explained to me why the school was illegal and told me why it was called a hedge school. But I soon found out that the school was not held in a field or behind a hedge but in an old barn, and Da had chosen Joe Cooney's hedge school for me. Even though Da explained everything to me, I couldn't understand why Catholics were singled out under the Penal Laws.

I would soon be at school every day, except Sundays. I decided to make the most of my time in the weeks before going. After I'd completed my jobs around the house and farm, I played with my friends in the fields. It wouldn't be long before I would be at school every day.

We were always up bright and early in the morning. One day we were chatting away around the kitchen table as we ate our breakfast. I was finding it difficult to keep my secret but I knew I must. Da had told me not to tell my siblings until everything had been arranged. I was excited about going to school and meeting other children so I found it hard not to tell anyone. I didn't understand what the secrecy was about. After all, it wouldn't be long and everyone would know all about it. I had to keep my mouth shut until Da had made the final arrangements.

We had only been living in the townland of Islands for a few years and hadn't had time to get to know all our neighbours. Da told me we couldn't trust anyone until we knew them better. He said that as the hedge schools were illegal, it was best not to talk about them. We didn't know who we could trust in those days. It was like that in the Penal Days in Ireland. We didn't trust anyone until we'd known them for some time. I was beginning to understand how difficult things were.

Just three weeks after Da had spoken to the priest, I happily started attending Joe Cooney's school. It was just a mile away from home. I walked there every day. Sometimes, if the weather was good, I took a shortcut through the fields. I took to learning quickly and was soon able to recite my numbers. It wasn't long before I was reading and writing my own name. The next problem for my parents was affording books for me to read. Mr. Cooney offered to lend me books. I enjoyed school but always looked forward to school holidays and the long summer evenings when I could meet up and play with my friends again.

Da had missed time at work while he had been looking for my teacher but now I was safely settled in school, he was able to catch up with several outstanding orders. He worked an 18-hour day to complete these. When he arrived home in the late evenings, Mam always had a meal waiting for him. By this time, we would all be in bed but Mam sat with him while he ate. She noticed more and more how tired Da was looking and she worried that he had more work than he could cope with.

One evening when Da had finished his meal, Mam said, "Have you thought any more about getting help in the workshop?" Da laughed and said, "We're so far out in the wilds there doesn't seem to be anybody I can ask. I've thought a lot about it lately and I'm hoping my brother, Thomas, will come and join us from Carrick. When we left, I said I would keep in touch. I'll write to him today. There's nowhere in the vicinity for him and his wife to live so we'd have to put them up in our house for a time. It'd be a bit of a squash but we'd manage. The other day I heard that the Flynn family in the little cottage next door might be emigrating. Their house will be vacant soon. It would be ideal for Thomas and his family. But they would have to live with us until the Flynns go."

Mam was pleased that Da had decided to call on the help of his brother.

"That's sounds a good idea, John. Quite apart from anything else it'll be lovely to have your brother's family living next door. Also, when he's not needed in the workshop, he'll be able to help on the farm. I'm looking forward to having his wife Nellie close by. I'm so glad. Let's hope they can come!"

Da agreed and said he hoped Nellie would help in the basket making. The two extra pairs of hands would make all the difference to our situation. Nellie would also be company for Mam.

So, Uncle Thomas and Aunt Nellie and their children came to live with us. Da and Mam moved into our bedroom and left the room over the parlour free for my uncle's family. It was a real crush in our bedroom. The worst thing was that Da sometimes snored and kept us awake. Da said they wouldn't be staying long so we looked forward to them moving out, and Da and Mam moving back to their own room.

Uncle Thomas was lucky as, six months later, the little cottage next to ours became vacant and he took the lease and moved in. We had become firm friends with our cousins and we were sorry to see them go. But they would only be next door so we would see them often. Our sleeping arrangements returned to normal and both families regained their privacy which was so much better.

CHAPTER FOUR

The years slipped by and I progressed at a fast rate at school. I seemed to be ahead of other pupils of my age. I was enjoying school and I loved learning my letters and learning to read. But I was glad when the holidays came around.

As we lived way out in the country, we rarely met anyone other than our close neighbours. I made several friends at school but I didn't see my them during the holidays or at weekends as we lived quite far apart.

We rarely had visitors at Islands. Occasionally, Sean the tinker came our way trying to sell his wares. He travelled far and wide and always brought news of happenings in other parts of the country. Each time he came we were eager to hear his tales. Around 1797, when I had been at school for three years, Sean brought unwelcome news to us. He told us tales of men wanting to rise up against the government. There was much discontent in the country because of the Penal Laws. Everyone thought that the laws, which only applied to Catholics, were unfair. It seemed so unjust – there were far more Catholics in Ireland than Protestants.

Sean said the unhappiness brought about by these laws was more marked in the north and west of Ireland than it was in the south where we lived. He told us many problems were caused by English landlords. They didn't even live in Ireland and relied on a manager to look after their estates. They were called absentee landlords. The managers, who were Irish and ran their estates for them, were harsh and unfair, and people were unhappy. The managers weren't interested in their tenants. Their main purpose in life was to make money for a master who lived in England. To do this they had to grow crops for export. They were forever expanding their cornfields and adding some poor family's small piece of land to theirs. Anyone who got behind with their rent could be evicted. When that happened, their home was destroyed and the land was taken over. Many families were pushed off the land like this. The only one to benefit was to the landlord who, with increased acreage, was now able to grow more crops. Every Irish man wanted to own some land of his own. This was far outside the grasp of most people. Catholics were not allowed to own property or land and they were very unhappy.

Sean told us about the hundreds of very poor people in Ireland. Numerous people lived in mud huts on tiny plots of land where all they could grow was potatoes. They worked for the landowners and received small wages. Their wages were saved to pay their rent. If they couldn't find work, they couldn't pay their rent. It was a tragic situation. In the summer months, they had to use some of their wages to buy food while they waited for the potato harvest to ripen.

Sean didn't think this unrest had reached us in the south east and hoped it might never do so but he was to be proved wrong. We were fortunate to weather the storms that lay ahead but many people didn't.

¤

We became aware of trouble brewing in the wider population from the occasional traveller who passed by our door. These travellers were young men looking for work. For them, a casual day's work here or there was better than nothing. But they wanted full time jobs. Irishmen were tired of the stranglehold the English seemed to have over our country. Da always listened to these tales and he understood the mood of the country.

Later, we heard that a group of men had got together and formed the United Irishmen. They were determined to make 'Ireland for the

Irish' and get rid of British rule. There would be a long struggle but these fierce patriots thought they could change the country overnight.

Several local men in Mullinahone joined this union and pledged to fight against the English establishment. We hated any signs of trouble. Mam and Da cautioned us not to go far from home. If we had to go out, we shouldn't talk to strangers. Da didn't want us involved with any agitators. One day Da was in Mullinahone and while he was there, he became aware of a strange atmosphere. There were gangs of young men standing on street corners. They had no work to go to. As he walked past one group, they all stopped talking. He said it was an eerie feeling and he was glad when he arrived home safe and sound.

Da told us about some of the very bad conditions he had witnessed in Mullinahone. Poverty seemed to be everywhere. Some labourers and their families lived in miserable conditions in huts on farmers' land. Others just lived by the roadside in makeshift huts. It was very distressing but Da just wanted us all to know about the problems faced by many people in Ireland. He was surprised at the things he witnessed in Mullinahone. We normally only went there for church and hadn't noticed these terrible conditions. This was the first time we became aware of how bad things were. At Islands, we were about three miles from Mullinahone and Da didn't think we were in any danger from the gangs.

At Islands all was quiet. We didn't think any of our neighbours were involved in the Union. This was one of the advantages of living out in the country. We enjoyed a quiet life and so did our neighbours. Da decided the family would stop going to Mullinahone every week for Mass. Instead, we went in the other direction, to Ballingarry, which was about three miles away to the west. I was glad we didn't live in a town and were away from all these troubles.

In the next weeks, we heard there were centres of discontent around the country, in particular in the counties of Wexford and Kildare. Towns in these counties had experienced days and nights of terror. People were living in fear and trembling as brutal torture was inflicted on some of the townspeople. Trouble seemed to be getting closer to us.

The Union was threatening to rise up against the British.

The Great Rebellion took place in 1798. The Union movement had started in the north of the country and was strong there. At first, we thought it strange that southerners were involved. But we soon realised it was religion which bonded the southerners with the men from the north. They were all fighting for the freedom to follow the religion of their choice. It wasn't surprising that the southerners became involved. Catholics wanted recognition and most of all wanted the Penal Laws repealed, so the southerners joined their northern brethren.

During the revolution that year, there were uprisings and battles in many parts of the country. Many men had joined the revolutionary army. The uprisings were suppressed by the militia, who were reinforced by units of the British Army. But many people were killed in these skirmishes.

Nothing happened close to home but there was an uprising in Cahir, County Tipperary, about 20 miles away from us. This was close enough for us to worry. We hoped nothing would happen in our area. Fortunately, the Cahir uprising was quickly crushed by the High Sheriff, aided by the police and the militia.

In County Wicklow, large numbers of men took part in a rural guerrilla war against the military and loyalist forces, and the area was plagued for several years by these rebels.

Battles broke out in New Ross in County Wexford and Cahir in County Tipperary, both nearer to us than those in County Wicklow. Da told us all to take care. These latest battles were too close for comfort. We stayed at home most of the time and didn't see any sign of the troubles. We were lucky to have plenty of land behind our house and we were able to spend a lot of our time there.

¤

Relief came in 1800 when the British government passed the Act of Union. This was passed largely in response to the rebellion but small parts of the great rebel armies of 1798 survived for a number of years and waged guerrilla warfare in several counties. The closest to us was in County Wicklow.

The Act of Union didn't come into force until January 1801 but, as far as we could see, it did little to help us. It was supposed to reduce the strength of the Protestants and it sought to reduce the harsh measures brought in by the Penal Laws, but it would take a long time for us to feel the effect of this new law.

As a result of the rebellion there had been many thousands of deaths throughout Ireland. In spite of the new Act, it looked as though it would be many years before we would see improvements in our lives.

One day, when we thought peace and calm had been restored, we were surprised to hear rumours of gangs of youths roaming and causing havoc in our neighbourhood. I heard about this from Joe Cooney at school. He was worried about how he would protect us if a gang arrived while he was teaching us. He made plans so we could all escape if trouble arose. At the first signs of any of these gangs approaching, Joe would bang three times on his desk and we would all escape through the back door into the fields. From there, we would have to make our way home, taking care not to be seen, hiding behind trees and in the bushes if necessary.

I went home and told Da about these arrangements. He was concerned for me as I would have to go a long way round to avoid trouble. I told him I wasn't worried and not to worry about me but Da was apprehensive about the mood in the country. He worried that the gangs might make their way to Islands so we would have to have a plan to cope with this.

For the next week, we all lived on tenterhooks, expecting the worst, but in the end all was quiet and we hoped the danger had gone away. We were not to be so lucky. Two weeks later I was in the fields helping Da and we heard a loud shout from the direction of the house. It was Mam. We wondered what was wrong.

Da shouted at me. "Get over behind the hedge and stay there. Don't move until I tell you it's all right to come out." I ran to the hedge and crouched down. I was about 100 yards from the house. As I peered through the hedge towards home, I could see Da making his way carefully towards our back door. He was moving cautiously, trying not to be seen. He was crossing a large open stretch of field so it wasn't easy for him. Eventually, I saw him go in through the back door. I was thankful he was safely home but I was left wondering what was happening.

I waited. I was too frightened to move. I heard shouts coming from the lane at the front of the house. I saw Da looking out, wondering where I was. He couldn't see me so he seemed satisfied. I stayed crouched behind the hedge. Da went back in and I heard raised voices again. I was trembling with fear as I had heard so many awful tales about these gangs of young men and how they tortured people.

Moments later, I saw a young man coming round the side of the house. He looked up at our thatched roof and shouted something to his friends. Three lads joined him and they were deep in conversation. I was too far away to hear what they were saying. They tried to open the back door but it had been barred against them. They banged furiously on the door but there was no answer. I thought of Da and Mam and my young sister and brothers who were inside and imagined they would all be frightened to death.

My worst fears were realised when I saw the first young man throwing a lighted torch on to our thatched roof which quickly caught fire. The lads all stood there, watching it and laughing. I wondered how they could be so evil.

The roof of our house was burning and there was nothing I could do about it.

I was filled with a deep fury and I was completely helpless. Then, thank God, it started to rain. But then the wind sprang up which helped to fan the flames. When the roof was well alight, the gang of boys ran off in the direction of Mullinahone. Then it rained even harder which thankfully seemed to quell the fire.

It was still pouring and from a distance I could see the rain had supressed the flames. It looked as if only part of the roof had burnt. I worried as I knew we didn't have money for repairs and Da would be devastated. After staying in my hiding place for another five minutes or so, I made sure the gang had gone and I ventured out.

I cautiously made my way back towards the house. As I got nearer, I could see the roof was still smoking. All was still and quiet. I imagined how tense the atmosphere must be inside. They would know from the smell that there had been a fire but they wouldn't know the roof had been damaged. I arrived at the back door and tried to get in but it was barricaded from the inside. I knocked and called out.

"Da, it's me! They've gone now." Within a few minutes, he moved the barrier and let me in.

"Are you sure they've gone?" he asked.

"They soon scarpered when they saw the damage they'd done. I think the rainstorm took them by surprise."

Da ventured out with me. I will never forget the look on his face when he saw the damage. He was distraught. He looked at me and said, "Well, that's put the cat among the pigeons! We haven't insured the house against fire. We never thought it was a risk out here in the country. We should have listened to the tally man and paid him to cover us when he was last here. Oh dear, oh dear, I must go inside and tell Mam what's happened."

We went inside and sat in the kitchen, discussing events and deciding what to do. Mam asked Da if our landlord would pay for the damage. Da was not hopeful.

"Probably not. He'll say we should have been more careful. More careful? He lives away in England and doesn't understand the problems we have here. Even if he was prepared to pay, it would probably take several months to get him to agree. If we want a secure roof over our heads, we'll have to find a way to pay for it ourselves."

The mood in the house was sombre. There was a feeling of helplessness about the place. Da said we should do something to protect what remained of the roof so I went out with him to see how bad things were. Most of the damage was out of sight and we couldn't see the extent of it. We needed a ladder.

Da had recently hurt his leg and wasn't able to climb the ladder to inspect the roof. It looked as though I would have to try. If I could manage, I would be able to tell Da the extent of the damage. I was glad he knew what to do as I had no idea. He was there to guide me. I had never done anything like this before.

We had about two or three hours of daylight left so we had to work quickly. Da went to fetch a ladder from the barn. He placed it up against the wall, under the worst part of the blackened thatch. He held on to it to keep it steady while I climbed up. I had a good look round and came down. We moved the ladder to another part and I climbed up again. Da waited for me to come down. As I got off the ladder, I said, "the damage doesn't seem to be too bad." I explained to Da what I had seen and told him the extent of the destruction. Da looked relieved. Things weren't as bad as he had expected.

"We must hurry now and remove all the burnt straw and try and get rid of it before nightfall," he said. "We must cover the gaping hole so the rain doesn't get in and ruin the rafters. It would be disastrous if we had another rain storm and the rain poured in through that open hole."

We could see more dark heavy clouds coming in our direction. Another rain storm would probably bring down the ceiling in the bedroom. I didn't know how we were going to manage.

Da went off to search in the barn and returned ten minutes later with a large sheet of canvas which had been used the year before to cover the haystack. I ran towards him and helped him carry it.

"This is just what we need. The problem now is finding a way to attach it to the remains of the roof. I think we'll have to nail it to the rafters."

When we least expected him, Joe Cooney arrived around the corner of the house. Never was I so pleased to see a visitor.

"I came to see how you are," he said. "Those thugs called at Widow Tobin's and frightened the life out of her. But – good news – the militia, who were recently established in Mullinahone, were called out and caught the gang after they left you. They are now in custody and will probably appear in court in a few days."

"I'm glad to hear they've been arrested, but it doesn't help us in our predicament," Da said.

Joe walked around the house and was amazed when he saw the damage.

"It seems as though I've come just in time. I'll help you get rid of the burnt straw and we'll nail the canvas over that hole."

Da borrowed another ladder from a neighbour, and Joe and I climbed up to the roof. We removed all the blackened thatch. There was little Da could do but he passed the nails and hammers to us. Joe and I were both working hard to cover the hole before nightfall. Da went inside and found Mam crying. He tried to comfort her but had difficulty finding the right words to say. The whole episode had been a terrible shock to us all.

I was so relieved Joe had turned up. Without him, I would never have managed to cover that hole by myself. He took care of the situation and made all the decisions. We worked hard together. When we had finished, we went inside and found Mam making supper. She asked Joe to stay for a bite. We all sat round the table and it was clear we had all suffered a shock.

"It'll take a little while for you all to get over this experience," said Joe. "I think you should stay at home for a few days, Richard, and help the family. For a ten-year-old, you've done a grand job. Not many boys your age would climb up a ladder and cope as you did. Well done."

We thanked Joe for his help and waved him off as he went down the lane.

When we went to bed that night, we had great difficulty sleeping. The wind was blowing under the canvas and through the rafters, making a strange whistling noise. At times, when the wind intensified, there was a loud howling noise which sounded like a pack of wolves. The whole family tossed and turned in their beds. It had been a terrible day and none of us slept well.

The next day, the priest called to see us. He'd heard of our trouble and said he would put out a request at Mass for people to help repair the roof. We were lucky. We had good neighbours and the following weekend they all turned up to fix the roof. After two days, the damage was repaired and the thatch replaced. It would have taken a long time to save up enough money for roof repairs. I knew it would be a long time before we forgot this setback.

The lads who had caused us so much trouble were kept in prison until their trial.

Da was called to give evidence. The judge passed a sentence which horrified everybody in the courtroom. He wanted to make an example of them. They were all found guilty and sentenced to be transported for life to Van Diemen's Land – the fate of many robbers and villains.

Da came home and told us what had happened.

"Well, let's hope others will be deterred from such behaviour. Some of their parents were in court and a big cry went up when the judge announced the sentence. When I left, crowds of people lined the streets. It will be a big story in the newspapers. Nothing like this has happened here before."

We were glad justice had been done but we would have to be very watchful in future.

Da said we must be on the lookout for strangers coming up our laneway. Travelling people tended to stick to the main roads leading to Ballingarry and Mullinahone and they didn't often call at our house. These travelling people had no permanent homes and several families moved around in groups. Most of them travelled on foot but occasionally we would see a traveller with a cart and pony. As well as looking for work, they were looking for a friendly farmer who would let them sleep in his barn. Some of them carried a tent which they used at night if they couldn't find a barn to sleep in

As they moved around the country, the men knocked on doors, offering to carry out repairs to things such as a bucket with a hole. They also offered to mend shoes. While their men were looking for work, the women and children in the group went from house to house, begging. Money was sparse and they led a hand-to-mouth existence.

There were other bands of travellers who travelled in caravans. The caravan people dealt in horses and asses. They sometimes passed through our district, and would spend a night or two by the roadside, having come to sell their horses at market. We'd see them from time to time on the main roads. They rarely came our way as our house was situated way off the main road. Sean the tinker and one or two very occasional travellers were the exceptions who did come up our lane.

CHAPTER FIVE

In the spring of 1800, Joe Cooney turned up at our house and talked to Da about my progress at school. He told Da he was pleased at how quickly I had learned to read and write. He said I had a thirst for knowledge and was always asking questions, and I showed a maturity beyond my years. Joe thought there was not much more he could teach me and suggested I would benefit from a more qualified teacher. He suggested I should go to a school in Thurles though he would be sorry to lose me as I had been a good example to the other youngsters and he enjoyed having me around.

Da was a bit taken aback when he heard what Joe had to say. He thought Joe's school was quite good enough for me.

"Tell me more about this other school. I'm interested but, more importantly, is it going to cost us more than we pay you now?" he said.

"It's a long story," Joe said. "You may have heard of Tom Cahill who lived in Callan? He ran a business making shoes and was well known in the area. At the time of the 1798 rebellion, he was accused of inciting the rabble. As you know, those were awful years and it was easy to get caught up in the uprising.

"I was living near Callan at the time and we lived in fear for our lives. We all went about our business quietly. Tom had done nothing wrong but was arrested and taken to the 'tripod' which had been erected in the town. He was tied up on it and flogged near to death as they thought they could extract secrets from him. Everyone knew he was innocent and fortunately a protestant clergyman intervened and spoke for him, and he was saved. His friends carried him to a place of safety and he was nursed back to health. His awful experience moved him so much he was determined to spend the remainder of his life helping others save their souls. When restored to health, he left Callan and moved to Thurles. He and two friends established themselves as 'monks', and they are now running a school for boys in the town. I know Richard would thrive in it."

Da had many more questions.

"Joe, I've never heard of this school. Why do you think Richard should go there? Will he be accepted? We don't even live in the town – they may not accept boys from elsewhere. What qualifications and knowledge do these teachers have?"

"John, I can assure you they are good educated Catholic men. Between them, they have vast knowledge. They don't just teach numbers and reading – they also teach Greek and Latin, and even geography, literature and other subjects. Living the life of monks they dedicate themselves to helping others worse off than themselves. Of course, they aren't *real* monks."

"I still wonder if they will accept Richard. We are nearly 20 miles from Thurles. Would Richard have to board with them? That round trip on a daily basis would be impossible."

"Yes, I expect he'll have to board with them. I'll find out for you. I'll recommend they accept him if you are agreeable."

"This has come like a bolt from the blue. You must give me time to think about it. It's a big step for the lad. But if it's good for him, I am halfway to agreeing. Give me time to ponder it."

"I will and, in the meantime, I'll make some more enquiries."

"Find out how much it'll cost to send Richard there, Joe."

"I've not looked into that. It'll surely cost you more than you are paying me now but if you can afford it, the boy is worth it. I'll let you know as soon as possible."

Da and Mam talked for some time about sending me away. They

talked late into the evening. Mam was loath to lose me but they both agreed if Joe Cooney thought it was the best move for me, how could they disagree? They talked about my prospects for the future. If I stopped my education now, my chances of finding a job would be few and far between. I would probably spend the rest of my life helping Da in the business or on the farm. They could see no other outlook for me. They knew farming wouldn't suit me. But with a good education, there might be other options open to me. At this stage, they had almost agreed that the school in Thurles would be good for me, but the last hurdle was the cost. Da waited for further news from Joe Cooney.

Da was always aware of the difficulties caused by the Penal Laws, particularly regarding education. Like so many other people, he lived in hope that one day the Act of Union would be properly enacted.

"You and I have only known one way of life," Da said to Mam. "Out here in the country, we avoid most of the troubles of the world. But like other people, as a result of these terrible laws, we have never had the chance to better ourselves. When the laws are fully repealed, it'll be a different world for our children and we must always bear that in mind. We must do the best we can for them. In future, education will be the best start in life we can give our children."

A week later, Joe Cooney came back to see Da with more news of the school in Thurles. He had made another trip there and had talked again to the monks.

"Come in," said Da. "What news do you have?"

"I had a long meeting with the monks," Joe replied. "You'll be pleased to hear they will accept Richard as a pupil. They told me some of the results they are having with other boys and they were very impressive. They emphasised how important it is for them to have bright pupils who will set a good example to others."

"Well, that sounds promising. But how much is it going to cost us?"

"Let me tell you the *really* good news. It will cost you no more than you are paying me now. In fact, it will be less of a burden as the fee they charge includes board and lodging on a five-day basis. Richard will be coming home at weekends so you won't be losing him completely."

Da was pleased with the news and said he would talk to Mam. When they had come to a decision, he would let Joe know. But I could tell he had already made up his mind.

When Joe left the house, Da breathed a big sigh of relief. He wanted the best for me and he knew if he sent me to Thurles, it was the best they could do. He couldn't wait 'til evening to discuss it with Mam.

It didn't take long for Da and Mam to agree I should be given this opportunity. It was now May and they agreed I should start school in September. I would go when the harvest had been collected in. They gave me the news the next day. I had just over three months to get used to the idea of going away from home and to prepare for my new school.

CHAPTER SIX

September soon arrived and Da took me to Thurles to start the next part of my life. I was now just 11 years old but felt very grown up going away to school. There was a tearful farewell from Mam as she hugged me goodbye.

"Look after yourself. It won't be long before you're back with us – only five days."

I grinned at her.

"It'll go by in a jiffy, Mam – just you see. I'll be back before you can say Jack Flash."

I gave her a hug and a kiss and jumped up on the cart with Da. He pulled on the reins and the donkey trotted away while I waved goodbye to Mam. My siblings came rushing out of the house to wave me off.

The journey to Thurles was through some interesting countryside. I had never travelled this road so everything was new to me. We passed many farms, most of which had finished their harvest and the stooks stood in the fields. The crows were encircling many of the wheat fields, pecking away at the ears of wheat which had fallen to the ground. We saw one or two scarecrows but they didn't seem to be a deterrent. The crows were having a good old feast.

It was fast approaching autumn and we could see blackberries and hazelnuts crowding the hedgerows. These were all ready for the picking but we didn't have time to stop and gather them.

The journey was a good one and we saw no other traffic on the road. We arrived in Thurles in good time and I was soon inside the school. Da bade me goodbye, left me, and made his way back to Islands.

I was shown around the school by one of the senior boys. He took me to the dormitory and showed me my bed. There were three dormitories and boys were allocated their space according to their age. I was in the middle dorm.

The first week at school went by quickly and in no time at all it was Friday and time for Da to come back to collect me.

At the end of the day, I came bouncing out of school and when I spotted Da, my face broke into a wide grin. He had arrived early and he sat in his little cart waiting for me to appear. I rushed towards him and threw my arms round him. It was a wonderful reunion. We were soon in the cart and on our way home. As we drove through the countryside, I was bubbling over with news about my first few days at my new school.

Da told me he had missed me and said he was looking forward to hearing all about my first week at boarding school. He was keen to hear how I had fared in my new surroundings.

"Da, you won't believe what I'm going to tell you. I'll be learning Latin! So, in future I'll know what the priest is talking about. I'll know more than you when we go to church. I had my first geography lesson and the teacher had a globe and showed us different countries around the world. Da, thank you for sending me there!"

I couldn't stop enthusing and I chatted all the way home.

"Richard, I'm glad you're making the most of your time at school. You never know where it will lead. Most of all, I'm pleased you're enjoying it."

It was a good journey home. When we arrived, the family came out to greet us. You'd think I'd been away for a year or two. They all rushed to hug me.

"Steady on, I've only been away for five days." We all laughed. Everyone had questions for me but I said, "Give me a chance. Let me get inside and we can talk." Da unharnessed the donkey and I helped him put the cart away then I led the donkey into the field.

We went inside and immediately I could smell the familiar smell of home cooking. Mam had made a special lamb stew for us and the family sat round the table enjoying the meal. Mam was keen to know more about the school.

"Richard, do they feed you well at school?"

"Not as well as you feed me, Mam, but fair enough. We have a lot of bread and potatoes to fill us up. We don't have many vegetables and we have meat on alternate days. But I always have a glass of milk with my meals. Some of the boys don't like milk and drink water. I look forward to supper time because they give us wonderful freshly baked bread with cheese."

"You've always liked cheese. I think I'll feed you up with meat and veg when you come home on weekends!"

And so, my school days progressed. But Da had a problem. He was losing a lot of time at work while he ferried me to and from school on Mondays and Fridays. One evening he said to Mam, "Missing two half days is costing us. I wish there was an alternative school for Richard nearer home. But the school suits him and I don't want to move him."

There was another problem which Da didn't mention to Mam. As the winter nights drew in, we were making the return journey in the dark. This was no fun on the quiet country roads. In some places, the road was little more than a dirt track and we had no light to show us the way. In other places, it was quite dangerous and once or twice we had been lucky the cart hadn't overturned.

I hated these journeys in the dark. I even started to worry about them before I came out of school.

Mam said, "I wonder if there is anyone else who makes regular trips to Thurles? We must ask around. It would be good if you could share with someone. Let's ask Father O'Brien when we next see him. He may know of someone."

"Good idea," said Da. "Even if I could get rid of one of the journeys, it would help. Let's see if he has any suggestions."

Father O'Brien didn't know of anyone going our way. But after enquiries were made around the district, we found a man who regularly travelled to Thurles on Monday mornings. It was not long before I was travelling with him but Da still had to fetch me at the end of the week.

At the end of term, I was offered a place as a permanent boarder so the weekly trips from Islands to Thurles stopped. Tom Cahill explained to Da that lessons would continue on Saturday mornings, followed by outdoor games and sports in the afternoon. Da could see the all-round benefits of the offer and he accepted it immediately.

I went off to school at the start of the new school year knowing I wouldn't be home until half term. Mam and Da waved me off and I looked forward to the new regime.

I had to get used to being at school at weekends. On Saturdays, we had sports. I have never been a fan of sports but they only lasted for an hour or two so I joined in. After a week in the schoolroom, the fresh air was good for me. Sundays were given over to religious duties and we revised our work in spare hours at the weekends.

As the school was in a town, I was glad to be shut away indoors away from any troubles. In the past few months, there had been trouble brewing in the wider population, particularly in towns. Bands of ruffians often roamed the streets causing trouble. The Irish Catholics were still unfairly treated and they were always agitating because it was taking too long to repeal the Penal Laws.

Nothing seemed to have been done to improve our lot since the Act of Union and this was causing unrest. More than anything, everyone hated the way the English dominated our country.

I hated any signs of trouble. The monks cautioned us not to go into the town because of unrest in the community. If we had to go, we weren't to talk to anybody or get involved with anyone. I had to go out once and I was very aware of a strange atmosphere. There were gangs of young men standing on street corners. I walked past one group and they all stopped talking as I passed. It reminded me of Da's experience a year or two ago in Mullinahone. It was an eerie feeling and I was glad to get back to school.

When I went home to Islands for the half term break, I told Da about my experience. He was surprised to hear things were bad in Thurles. He said there were centres of discontent around the country but he didn't realise it had reached this far. I told him not to worry as we weren't in danger because we stayed indoors most of the time. I hadn't been out since that one occurrence and he was pleased to hear this. Meanwhile, at Islands all seemed quiet. Da didn't think any of our neighbours were involved in the Union. This was a relief to me as I realised I needn't worry about my family when I was away. One of the benefits of living in the country was the scarcity of neighbours who in any case were all farmers and their one interest was the land and their crops. They had no time for politics. I was glad we didn't live in a town.

CHAPTER SEVEN

It was 1807 and I was sixteen years old. It was now time for me to leave school. I had enjoyed my years in Thurles but these were coming to an end. It would soon be time for me to decide what to do with my life. Until now, I had not thought about how I would spend my time after school. I wondered if I would have to leave home to find work. The last time I was at home, Da had said there was no rush to make a decision and told me to take my time.

On my last day at school, the master, Mr. Cahill, asked me into his study.

"Well, Richard, the time has come for you to leave us. I know you've benefited greatly from your time here. Your education has been the groundwork for your future life, whatever it may be. But I want to put a proposition to you. How would you like to stay here at school as a monitor? Your duties would be to teach the younger boys. I have every confidence in you. Give my offer some thought over the summer and let me know what you think. You don't have to answer straight away. We would pay you a small wage if you decide to take up this offer. There's no need to make an immediate decision but I would like to know your answer in good time before the autumn term starts."

I was astounded at Mr. Cahill's offer. I'd never expected to find a job so soon. Many thoughts went through my mind all at once: Da would no longer have to pay my school fees and I would be able to contribute to the family budget from my small wage. I thanked Mr.

Cahill very much for the offer and said I would discuss it with my parents and would let him know as soon as possible. I already knew what my answer would be so I had no need to discuss it with Mam and Da. I loved the school environment and nothing could be better than teaching young boys how to read and write. I couldn't believe how lucky I was and I whistled to myself as I made my way to Da, waiting outside as usual with the donkey and cart.

I lost no time in telling him about Mr. Cahill's offer. Da was amazed and kept chuckling to himself. He turned to me and said, "We've been richly rewarded by sending you to Thurles. Well done, my boy. I hope you're going to accept this wonderful offer?"

I looked at Da.

"There's nothing I would like better so yes, of course, I will be accepting it."

We journeyed on for a few more miles, both in silence with our own thoughts. As we were nearing home, I turned to Da and said, "You know where this might lead, don't you?" Da looked puzzled. I continued "Well, after a year of teaching in Thurles I will be free to do what I like. Perhaps I will set up my own hedge school at Islands."

Da was surprised to hear this and didn't know what to say for a few minutes, but muttered, "There's our old barn which would make a good school!" He was obviously filled with pride and couldn't wait to get home and tell Mam the good news.

We arrived home as the sun was setting behind our house. There were no clouds in the sky and the pinks and reds stretched from the south, through the west to the north. It was a very pretty sight and I was glad to be home.

We were soon inside and Da was proudly telling Mam of Mr. Cahill's offer.

Mam was delighted.

"Does this mean you are to live away from us again? Just as I was getting used to the thought of having you home again. Never mind; I know it's for the good."

A few weeks later, I accepted the teaching position. I went back to Thurles in September to take up my job. It was good to be back but strange to be at the other end of the classroom! I soon got used to it and, although I was only a monitor – or student teacher – I was well versed and able to answer all questions from my students. I was soon respected by my pupils and I went about my daily chores with a smile on my face. For me, life had never been so good. I was free of home responsibilities and felt liberated. I had boundless energy and my mood of optimism transferred to everyone I came in contact with. Mr. Cahill said the school in Thurles was a happier place since I had joined the staff.

All too soon my year at Thurles was coming to a close. When it was nearing the end of the summer term, Mr. Cahill told me he was keen to keep me on as a teacher. He offered me a position with double my wages. It was an enticing offer. I thanked him and asked him if I could think about it for a few days.

I gave his offer some serious thought. The extra money was a great temptation but I was keen to set up my own hedge school at Islands. I mulled it over; it was difficult to turn down Mr. Cahill's offer but I thought I would be much happier running my own school at home. It would give me greater satisfaction than working for someone else. I was confident my school would do well as there was no competition from other schools in the vicinity of Islands and I was sure that plenty of young people would benefit.

After a few days, I sadly turned down Mr. Cahill's offer but thanked him for the wonderful opportunity he had presented to me. He was disappointed at my response but said he was pleased to hear my plans. He was glad I was going to continue to pass on my knowledge to other youngsters. He wished me luck in my new venture. At the end of term, as I said goodbye, we agreed to keep in touch. He made it clear I could contact him if ever I needed help in any way.

When I finally left Thurles at the end of term, I told Da I had definitely decided to go ahead with my hedge school. He was pleased to hear my decision.

"Don't forget I said you can use the old barn as a schoolroom. It'll be a roof over your head. But it'll be cold in winter and the youngsters will have to keep their coats on."

I laughed.

"I'll include some physical exercise in their timetable so I'll have them jumping up and down every hour. That'll keep them warm."

"The barn is ten times better than the mud hut I went to in Carrick," said Da. "Let's go and tell your mother what you've decided."

Mam was pleased when I told her I was returning home for good. As usual, she had made a special supper for my homecoming and all the family sat round the table, enjoying the party atmosphere. My younger siblings had all grown apace in my years away. I looked around at my family and realised I would not only be teaching our neighbours' children but also my younger brothers and sisters.

During the time I had been away at school, the troubles of the previous years seemed to have settled down. Even though we had the new Act of Union, the difficulties caused by the Penal Laws were still with us. But the constabulary, many of whom were Catholics themselves, tended to look the other way when they heard about illegal schools as long as we didn't make any trouble. They also turned a blind eye to any religious events. As a result, loyal Catholics were able to pray and take Mass and go to their illegal hedge schools. We wondered when times would change and this new law would be fully enacted.

CHAPTER EIGHT

My school was soon up and running in the barn. My younger siblings had been keen to be involved and helped me prepare it ready for the start of term. We made six long benches out of oak wood, each of which would hold six children at a squash, so there was room for about 36 youngsters in total.

I worried that the barn was rather dark as it had no windows. Even with the door open there was not enough light to enable youngsters to read and write. I shuddered at the thought of the cost of candles and decided there must be another solution to this problem. In the middle of winter, it would be too cold to keep the door open to let the light in. I decided to cut a large hole in the side of the building. The opening would create a draft but I would cut it on the opposite side of the prevailing wind and hoped it wouldn't be too bad. One day, one or two parents turned up to help me. When we had finished cutting, the light came streaming in. I was pleased with it and looked forward to the day when I could afford to have glass installed in the hole but that would have to wait. The barn was now ready for lessons.

People from far and wide soon heard about my school. The Frisby children were the first five on the register but the number soon rose to 20. So, I became a hedge teacher and I loved teaching, not just my siblings, but also other youngsters from the immediate neighbourhood. My pupils were all keen and eager to learn and they had a thirst for knowledge denied to them by law.

To start with, I only taught numbers, reading and writing. I wanted to progress further in other subjects but didn't want to put the cart before the horse as all my pupils were starting from scratch. Da frequently walked down to the barn to see how we were getting on. As he came towards us, he could hear the chanting of the alphabet ringing out loud. The first thing I taught them after they had learned the alphabet was how to write their own names. They were fascinated and scribbled them non-stop!

I envisaged them going home and proudly showing their parents how clever they were. I soon moved them on to harder work. It was a good start and I was pleased with their progress.

I included religious instruction in my syllabus, for half an hour first thing every morning. I didn't have to cater for other religions as all my pupils were from Catholic backgrounds. When I was in school at Thurles, I thought too much time was spent on religious instruction. Children quickly became bored and lost interest. Half an hour a day was sufficient. We studied Bible stories and sang hymns. At Thurles, we had been instructed in other religious matters such as praying with the Rosary but I didn't include this in my lessons as I decided my pupils should be taught about the Rosary by their parents.

We were getting close to Christmas towards the end of the first term and I decided to include some light form of entertainment for the children. They made a wee crib with the baby Jesus in it which they designed and made themselves, with little guidance from me. They were proud of the result. Diversions like this, from time to time, were good for the children. When they returned to their work, they tended to study harder. At the end of term, we had a Christmas party. Mam made mince pies for us which were enjoyed by all and we sang carols. It was a good ending to my first term.

In January, when we were just into our second term in the barn, it started to snow! I had only seen snow twice in my lifetime. It was a rarity in our part of the country. The children were delighted as they had never seen snow before. But the following days became difficult as it snowed so hard that the lanes were almost impassable. Children were kept at home as it was tough for them to walk in the deep snow. For three weeks the only children I taught were our family members. The bad weather lasted for weeks. That year was named 'The Year of the Big Snow'. It will be remembered for a long time.

The children in our family enjoyed this change in the weather and they were delighted that I closed the school early most days. They wrapped up warm and were outside playing the usual games. Their favourite game was throwing snowballs. It was not long before several rival snowmen had popped up at the back of the house.

After a few hours outside, the children were freezing cold and ran back to the house to warm themselves by the kitchen fire and to have a hot drink. Not far from us was a very low hill and it provided a grand slope for tobogganing. They made all sorts of toboggans from pieces of wood and metal which they found lying around. After a while, boredom and cold brought them back indoors.

Fortunately, when spring came it soon warmed up and the weather was back to normal. I had a full complement of pupils and I decided they would spend an hour each day outside. During the weekends I had prepared a patch of land and I wanted to encourage the children to grow vegetables there. I wondered if my idea would take off as all the children came from farming backgrounds. They might already be growing vegetables at home. But I was surprised at their enthusiasm. I think they were pleased to go out into the fresh air and get away from lessons for a short while. This soon became a regular feature. Living alongside the monks in Thurles had made me realise how important it was to be self-sufficient. This subject was an important part of our syllabus.

One of the largest crops grown in Ireland is our staple diet – the potato - so I decided it would be a good crop for the children to grow first. Of course, they all grew potatoes at home and they thought it would be easy.

I gave them a short lesson on gardening before we went outside. I told them there were several different methods of propagation and listed them on my slate. I drew diagrams of roots, bulbs, rhizomes and tubers. I told them the one they were going to learn about was the tuber. I told them a tuber was a swollen underground stem with several buds on it and I explained to them that the potato was a tuber.

I had sketched on my large slate a description headed, "The Potato", showing bad things and good things about it. To make it more interesting, I included in this a list of the bugs which were likely to attack potatoes such as the click beetle and the wireworm.

I explained we would be planting potatoes in a patch of land I had already prepared. The children were all eager to get outside. We started by digging drills for the potatoes. We only had 4 spades and they were soon fighting over who would go first. All in all, it was a success. But, having started gardening, I had to continually decide what to teach them next. Thankfully they were not slow in coming forward with ideas. By summer we had a thriving garden and some very good little gardeners.

By the end of my first year as a hedge teacher I had 23 pupils. About eight children were receiving free education. These were my siblings and those whose parents couldn't afford to pay the fees. These parents were keen for their children to be educated and I couldn't turn them away.

There was no way I was going to charge Da for my siblings. Da insisted on paying me but I said, "No, Da, you've provided the barn for our use and we have the freedom of the fields. This offsets any unpaid fees." He eventually accepted my reasoning.

One day I realised boys greatly outnumbered girls in the school. My two young sisters were keen learners and had persuaded three of their friends to join them at school. But the balance was still wrong with only five girls and 18 boys. So, I set about trying to encourage the boys to bring their sisters to school. One day, Martin Walsh, a little boy of seven, came to see me.

"Sir," he said, "I tried to get my sisters to come to school but Ma says we can't afford to educate them as well as me. Ma and Pa think girls don't need an education."

"Would you like me to talk to them, Martin?" I said. "I won't say you've come to me about it. What do you think?"

"Yes please, sir. That would be good. Thank you."

I went to see Mr. and Mrs. Walsh the following weekend. They lived in a cottage about half a mile from us. It was a pleasant walk on a balmy evening. When I arrived, I was amazed to see the patch of land next to the house was teeming with kids. Martin saw me coming and ran up to me.

"Hello, sir, have you come to see Ma and Pa?"

"Yes, Martin, are they at home?"

Martin took me inside and introduced me to his sister, Mary, who was much older than the other children and the eldest in the family.

She was busy in the kitchen, helping her mother. She must have been only a couple of years younger than me. She was a bonnie lassie and greeted me kindly then introduced me to her mother.

"Shall I be making you a drink?" she asked. I asked for a drink of cold water as I was quite hot after walking in the lanes. The back door opened and her father came in. After the usual greetings, we got down to business. I told them Martin was a good student and was doing well in all subjects.

"We were amazed the other day when he came home and showed us he could write his own name," Mr. Walsh said. They were pleased he had learned this so quickly.

After a while, I explained to them that I wanted to see more girls at school. I told them I believed girls and boys should have the same education. None of us knew what lay ahead. Nothing would be more useful to young children than to be able to read and write. They seemed surprised at my views.

"Some people say my ideas are radical but I believe that by the time our children get into their twenties or even thirties life will be very different here in Ireland."

Mr. Walsh was not slow in replying.

"I can see your point of view but we just can't afford to send more children to school. We just don't have that money."

I explained to him that he needn't worry as I had a plan to reduce the fees when we had more than one child from the same family. I was even prepared to waive the fees for 2nd and 3rd children if parents couldn't afford to pay. He looked very surprised.

All the time we were talking Mary, Martin's sister, was sitting in the background and listening to our conversation. When Mr. Walsh said he would think about it, I saw a smile creep over Mary's face. She knew I might have won her father over. I said I was glad to hear he was not totally opposed to the idea and I got up to go. Mary said she would show me out. She took me to the front door and walked to the lane with me. We stood there talking for a while and when I bade her farewell, I was sorry to go. As I walked home, Mary was on my mind. She was a very attractive girl with a wonderful fresh complexion. I had enjoyed the very short time I was with her and I hoped I would be seeing her again soon.

A week later, Martin turned up at school with two of his sisters. I was pleased to see them and it wasn't long before they were enjoying their time at school. On most days their elder sister Mary came to meet them and walk them home. I was glad as I didn't think I would be seeing her so soon after my visit to her house. We always had time for a short chat and we got on well. Gradually, we struck up a firm friendship and we started walking out together in the evenings. I had never had a girlfriend before. Mam and Da noticed our friendship and were pleased with the way things were going.

CHAPTER NINE

At the end of my first school year in the barn, I decided to make a trip back to Thurles and visit my old school. It was a lovely day in mid-August and I set off on my horse early in the morning.

I can't explain how free I felt as I rode along the lanes. The air was fresh and the sun was hot in a blue sky. I hadn't realised how glad I would be to get away from the barn. Three terms of constant teaching had tired me. It was only when I was out on the open road that I realised how drained I had become. I made a promise to myself to get out more often. In the past year, when I wasn't teaching, I had helped out on the farm. It was always good to get out into the fresh air.

I arrived in Thurles mid-morning and tethered my horse before knocking on the school door. Tom Cahill answered the door.

"Why, hello, my boy, how good to see you! Come on in. Is everything all right?"

I quickly assured him everything was fine and said, "I've just finished my first school year so I decided to pay you a visit."

We were soon sitting down inside and Joe was keen to hear everything about my school and wanted to know how it was going. I told him all about it and he said he'd always known I would be successful. I asked him how he was getting on. He hesitated before replying, "It could be better. We've certainly missed your help but with the grace of God things will improve."

His guarded reply told me he there were some problems and I said I was sorry if he had difficulties. He told me not to worry.

"I know everything will work out well," he said. He sounded confident. Then he proceeded to ask me if I had heard of Edmund Rice.

I already knew a little about Edmund Rice who came from the town of Callan just over the border in County Kilkenny. He went on to tell me that he had lost his wife in a house fire a few years ago. His young daughter had been badly injured in the tragedy and was now an invalid. After the trauma of that and losing his wife, he decided to give up business life and concentrate on helping the poor and looking after his daughter.

"Like us, he moved away from Callan to start a new life. He went to Waterford and eventually set up a school for the poor children of the town."

I enjoyed listening to Joe's tale but wondered why he was so interested in Rice. I was soon to find out. Joe said he had visited Edmund in Waterford and was amazed by what he had achieved in a very short time.

"I thought, 'What a coincidence! He's living the life of a monk like we are!'"

It was obvious the two men had a lot in common and they promised to keep in touch. Edmund offered to help Joe in any way he could. So now I knew why Joe was so confident that everything would be all right. He even said, "There's a probability we'll be working with Edmund Rice in the future."

After our chat, Joe took me on a tour of the school and showed me the improvements he'd made in the year since I'd left. The school was doing well, with over a hundred pupils. It was an interesting visit.

As I rode home from Thurles, I thought about Joe. From what he told me of Edmund Rice I was sure their union would be a good one. I wondered when I would hear more about their cooperation.

¤

That evening after supper, I visited Mary Walsh and we walked out together in the direction of Mullinahone. We strolled near the

King's River and found a shady spot under a beech tree on the river bank where we sat and talked. Mary was the eldest of nine younger brothers and sisters and she spent most of her time helping her mother. Laundry days were always the busiest and she said most of her time was taken up with sewing. Clothes had to be mended or altered for the children. The younger children always wore hand-me-downs which had been altered many times. She was very domesticated and I teased her.

"You sound like a mother hen." She laughed and said she had never known anything else.

As we sat there, the sun was going down and a shaft of light fell on Mary's face. I looked at her and I thought again how pretty she was. I had a great desire to kiss her so I leaned towards her and kissed her on the cheek. At first, she was a little taken aback but she responded. She smiled at me and we were happy. Later, she told me how glad she was that Martin and her young sisters had the chance of an education which she never had herself. I then realised she couldn't read or write. I felt sorry for her.

"Would you like to be able to read and write?" I asked her. She said there was nothing she would like more. I was quiet for a while, then replied, "I have an idea. Would you like a small job with me? I need someone to tidy up the barn at the end of each school day. If you could help me, I could repay you by teaching you to read and write. How's that for a plan?"

Mary was taken aback by my offer and didn't know what to say. I told her to think about it and let me know if she was interested.

"Richard, it's a wonderful idea. I don't need to think about it. When can I start?"

I was becoming very fond of Mary and by offering to teach her, I realised I would see her more frequently. I was surprised at my feelings as I had never had any like this before, though I suppose I hadn't met many girls my age.

I couldn't wait to start Mary's lessons but realised this would have to wait until the start of the new term. But we were both so keen on the idea that we started early and I spent my summer holidays with my 'private' pupil. Mary was a fast learner. By the end of the holidays, she was able to read a little and could even write her name.

My offer of a job still stood and when the new term started, Mary came to the barn an hour before the end of the school day to help me out and her learning continued.

It was not long before I realised how warm our relationship was. I knew then that I loved her dearly. We spent a lot of time together in term time. In the school holidays when I'd finished helping around the farm and she'd finished helping her mother, we met in the evenings and went for a stroll together. Life had never been so good.

I remember our walks along the bank of the King's River. Many times, we stopped and sat in the light of the setting sun and held hands. One day, I held her in my arms and looked into her beautiful face.

"You're so beautiful," I said. "You have lovely hazel eyes and I love you so much." Mary laughed and teased me.

"You're an old romantic!" she said.

But our good life was soon to be interrupted. One day, Martin and his sisters didn't turn up at school. Mary came to see me in the evening and she was in tears.

"Whatever's the matter?" I asked.

"Rich, I can't believe what's happened. My dear mother passed away last night. It was like a bolt from the blue. She's always been so healthy but she was taken ill during the evening with a pain in her chest so we called the doctor. She was gone before he arrived; he said she died from a heart attack."

"Come here," I said and I took her in my arms. She sobbed on my shoulder and I tried to pacify her. There was nothing I could say or do to make her feel better.

Mary's mother's untimely passing brought to an end the times we were able to spend together. I wanted to help her but she was so bound up with looking after her family we rarely saw each other. I realised how deep my love was for her and I missed our evening walks. We always met after Mass on Sundays but things never seemed the same. Mary was withdrawn and seemed to carry the weight of the world on her shoulders. While she was so anxious and depressed, there was nothing I could do to help her. I would have to wait until her terrible grief had passed.

CHAPTER TEN

The years passed by and in 1812 I went to Callan to buy some books for the school. I had ridden there on our old horse. On my way home, I was nearly at our house when I saw someone walking towards me. It was Mary and I was so pleased to see her. I jumped off the horse and ran towards her. She had a big smile on her face. I took her in my arms and gave her a hug. She was taken aback and we both laughed.

Mary told me that two of her brothers had left home and gone to work in Dublin. She now had more time to herself. I could see immediately from her expression that she had recovered from her grief and depression. It had taken a long time but I thanked God she was better.

I realised I wanted to spend the rest of my life with Mary. This had been in my thoughts for some time, but the death of her mother had put a stop to everything. I decided I would ask her to marry me the next day.

I rose early the following day and was soon dressed and ready to go out.

"Where are you going so early?" asked Mam.

"I have a special errand to do," I said. "I'll tell you about it when I get home."

Mam looked surprised as I always told her everything. It was not like me to keep secrets from her. Off I went, waving.

"Good-bye, see you soon."

I made my way straight to the Walsh's house. I knocked on the door and Mary's father opened it.

"Hello Mr. Walsh," I said. "Is Mary at home?"

"Wait a while," he said. "I'll fetch her."

Mary arrived at the door and was clearly surprised to see me so early in the day, but even more surprised when I got down on one knee and said, "Mary, my darling, will you marry me?"

She was taken aback by my proposal. It was a few minutes before she could say anything and she held her two hands to her face in surprise.

"Of course I will! I thought you'd never ask!"

I jumped up and flung my arms around her.

"Thank you, thank you!" I said. "You've made me so happy!" I embraced her and we kissed on her doorstep. Mr. Walsh came out and when he saw us kissing, he said, "It's a bit early in the morning for that, isn't it?"

Mary turned round and said to her father, "Pa, we're getting married!"

"I see," Mary's father grunted and continued out to his garden. I looked at Mary and smiled.

"Don't worry. It's probably a bit of a shock for him but he'll come round in due course."

I rushed home and gave the good news to Mam. All the family were delighted. They all really liked Mary.

But I was to have a surprise the next day when Mary called early in the morning.

"I've something to tell you."

"What is it?" I said, looking surprised.

"Can we go somewhere quiet and sit down?"

We made our way towards the barn and sat on a fallen log outside.

"Well," I said. "What's so important to bring you here so early in the morning?"

Mary started to cry and I wondered what on earth was wrong. I put my arm around her shoulder.

"Hush now, don't take on so. What's upset you?"

"Richard, Pa won't let me marry you!"

"Why ever not? What have I done wrong?"

"You've done nothing wrong. It's just him. He's so difficult. Ever since Mama died, he's relied on me to do everything. I cook for him and I wash his clothes. I clean his house and I look after the young ones. He's never satisfied. And now he thinks he's going to lose me. It's so unfair! He truly believes it's my duty to stay at home and look after him forever. Well, I won't! He's been so disagreeable there's no way I'll stay now. Let's see how he gets on when I'm gone!"

I was stunned by this turn of events and hoped we could find a way through the problem.

"Mary, my love," I said. "He was obviously taken by surprise when you told him the news. We must let him cool down and get used to the idea. When the dust has settled, we must talk to him together. I'll come with you to see him in a few days."

Mary wiped her eyes and said she thought her father would never give in. But I told her she was of age and he wouldn't be able to stop her leaving home. On hearing this, she brightened up a little. The whole episode had left a bitter taste in our mouths. It spoiled the joy we had experienced the previous day. I was determined we would marry.

"Your father doesn't own you," I said. "He doesn't deserve you. He's been very lucky to have your help in the last few years. We *will* marry – and soon!"

Mary was relieved to hear this and after a little while, feeling better, she got ready to make her way home. As always, she would be going home to make dinner for her father and the family. I really did believe that he didn't deserve to have her.

After I had kissed her goodbye, I waved her off down the road. When she was out of sight, I went inside and told Mam what had happened. She wasn't surprised and said she'd seen it coming.

"When a man loses his wife at such an early age, he is stricken with grief. He can see nothing in the future. But he soon realises he has a family to care for and he'll take any help he can get. Mary has been helping the family for too long. Many young girls fall into this trap and end up looking after their families all their lives. Poor lass, she needs a break. She deserves better than that."

Mam said she had seen many cases like this in her youth. Even her own elder sister had stayed at home to look after her parents and had never married. She told me not to worry. I thought that if we were determined enough things, would have a way of working themselves out. I had not been so unhappy for years.

The following weekend we went to Mass in Ballingarry in the field next to the ruined church. Afterwards, Mary and I made our way back to the Walsh homestead. When we arrived, Mary took me in and said she thought her father was in the kitchen. Like most homes in Ireland, the kitchen was the hub of the household and used for cooking, eating and also as a sitting room. The parlour was only used on special occasions. I wiped my boots before going in and Mary led me into the kitchen.

"Hello Pa," she said. "Richard and I have come to talk to you."

Mr. Walsh looked taken aback. He hadn't expected Mary to bring me to see him. He said hello and offered me a chair. I sat down and there was an awkward silence.

"I suppose I know what brings you here," he said.

I cleared my throat.

"Mr. Walsh I've come to ask you for the hand of your daughter in marriage. Will you give me permission to marry her?"

There was a long silence.

"I'll miss her, you know. She's a great help to me in the house. Since my dear wife died, she's been the backbone of this family. Of course I don't want her to go but I can't think of anyone I'd rather have as a son-in-law. So, yes, you can marry her and with my good wishes to you both."

Mary and I were surprised at her father's change of heart. Mary went over to her father and put her arms around his neck, saying. "Thank you, Pa. I love you, you know," she added. "I'm sure I'll be back from time to time to help you."

"Good," he replied. "Well, that's that. When's the wedding?"

"Oh Pa, we haven't given it any thought. But now you've agreed, we won't be leaving it too long."

Later, I asked Mary where she wanted to live when we were married. Like me, she hadn't thought about it. We talked about various possibilities but came to no conclusion. I went home and gave the good news to Mam and she immediately said, "Where will you both live?" I laughed and said, "I don't know."

"Would you like to live here, if we make a few changes?" Mam said.

I couldn't imagine how we could possibly squeeze in with the family.

"What do you have in mind?"

"When Da and I married, back in Carrick-on-Suir, we moved into his parents' cottage," she said. "That seems to be a family tradition so perhaps we should stick to it. You and Mary can have the room over the parlour to yourselves."

I was stunned by Mam's generosity. We only had two bedrooms but Mam was suggesting this because I was the oldest son. It was a family tradition passed down through the generations and Mam said it was good for the family to keep the eldest son at home if possible. By custom, he always took over the house after his parents passed.

I was amazed we had solved the problem so quickly. I kissed Mam and thanked her for her kindness. But I worried about how the family would cope, all in one bedroom.

"I hope you won't all be too crowded, cramped up in one room."

"Don't you worry about us," Mam replied. "We'll manage and we'll be hoping it won't be long before you have your own wee ones sharing your room."

I wondered if it was this a good solution … Mam said it had worked well in the past so who was I to argue? Only time would tell.

I soon told Mary the good news and she was amazed at my family's generosity. I teased her, saying she was lucky to be marrying the eldest son!

CHAPTER ELEVEN

We had a quiet wedding and afterwards we went home to Islands where we partied with a few neighbours. Uncle Thomas and Aunt Nellie, who had moved up from Carrick, joined us. Uncle Thomas played the fiddle and I was really glad they had come as they livened up the event. We had a wonderful evening with lots of dancing and singing.

I was surprised when my cousin David Frisby turned up. He was my uncle Thomas' son and lived in Ballyduggan in the shadow of Slievenamon, near Mullinahone. I hadn't seen him for several years. We were all pleased to see him. I asked him how he knew about the wedding.

"News travels fast in the country!" he said.

David was the same age as me and we got on well. He was a very go-ahead young man and had taken over his father's farm. It was his father, Thomas Frisby, who had encouraged us to move to Islands years ago. David's landholding at Ballyduggan was large and he spent most of his time out in the fields tending his flocks of sheep and other animals. With 20 acres to look after it was unusual for him to take time out so we were especially pleased to see him. He had recently been widowed and had four children but a good friend in his village was looking after them while he visited us.

The party lasted late into the night with much dancing and merriment. One of our neighbours played the pipes alongside Uncle Thomas. Mam had made food and Da brought in a supply of poitín and cider. We were exhausted by the end of the day and it was after midnight when we made our way to our new bedroom.

The next day, the whole family slept late. Normally everyone was up and about by six o'clock. It was nearly nine o'clock when we all had breakfast together. I asked Mary if she had any ideas about what she wanted to do that day. She said she was quite happy to have a quiet day. We were still in the school holidays and I thought we both deserved a little time off. I decided to take her out and about for a day or two before getting back to our normal routine.

The following day we were up early and borrowed the donkey and cart from Da. It was a lovely day and Mary and I set off towards Ballingarry. Mary asked me where I was taking her and I told her I thought a trip to Thurles would be good. She had never gone far in her short life – Mullinahone and Ballingarry were the extent of her travels. The 20-mile journey to Thurles would be new to her and I wanted to show her where I went to school. After that, we could have a look around the shops. I was hoping I would have time to talk with Tom Cahill to see how the school had progressed since my last visit.

The journey to Thurles went by quickly as we chatted all the way. The countryside was looking lovely in the summer sun and Mary was enthralled with these new surroundings. As we travelled, we talked about our future and our hope to have children.

"It looks as if you'll be teaching your own children. There never seems to be an end to the relatives attending your school." We both laughed at this.

We arrived in Thurles and went straight to the school. I knocked on the door with the heavy cast iron door knocker and a few seconds later it opened and there stood Tom Cahill. He was surprised to see us and ushered us in to his office.

"Tom, I want to introduce you to my wife, Mary. We were married two days ago."

Tom beamed his usual smile and shook hands with Mary, saying, "I'm pleased to meet you, Mary. I hope you'll both have a long and happy marriage and that God will bless you with children."

I noticed Tom looked different. After a few moments I realised why. He was dressed in different clothing and now he really did look like a monk. I asked him if he had any news and he replied, "Well, yes, I have quite a lot to tell you."

The burden of running the school had started to take its toll on Tom and his brother William. With over 100 pupils, they were finding it difficult to manage without help. Tom remembered his visit to Waterford and Edmund Rice's offer of help. He reminded me that Edmund had pledged to devote his life to the education of the poor. As well as setting up a school in Waterford, he had been training teachers and he now had two schools in Waterford. In 1806, he had opened others in Carrick-on-Suir and Dungarvan. In 1808, Edmund took religious vows and formed the Presentation Brothers, a new congregation of monks.

All Edmund's schools were run by the new Presentation Brothers. He hoped to spread the word of the Brothers and his methods of teaching throughout Ireland.

"I expect you can see where this is going," Tom said. I nodded and he went on to say he and his brother William had visited Edmund in Waterford again. They were very impressed by all they saw and were now seriously considering entering the brotherhood themselves. If they did, their school would be run under the auspices of Edmund Rice and the Brothers. They were planning to go to Waterford to train as monks.

I was astounded to hear these new arrangements. When I thought about it later, I was not very surprised. I knew from personal experience how many hours of religious instruction they taught in Thurles. Now I realised just how devout these men were. Mary sat quietly beside me all the time Tom was talking and I wondered what she thought of these revelations.

Tom was keen to know how my school was progressing. I told him about the barn and how I was encouraging girls as well as boys to join us. He was surprised to hear my thoughts as he only taught boys. I told him I thought it was important that girls were able to read and write too.

"In years to come, girls will have to go out to work like boys, so they will need to be able to read and write," I said.

We had a long discussion about this. I could tell Tom didn't agree with me but I stuck to my guns, telling him all the girls in our family were now being educated. He was surprised and ended by saying, "Maybe you're right. We can't accommodate girls but we must keep abreast of the times." I thought I had gone some way to persuading him but we left it at that.

After telling us his news, Tom took us on a tour of the school and showed us the improvements they had made since I last visited. I was most impressed. It was soon time to go and, as we were leaving, Tom and I agreed to keep in touch. I was keen to know how they would fare in future. It had been an interesting few hours.

We made our way into Thurles town and Mary was delighted with the shops. She had never been in a large town and was amazed at the variety. I decided to buy her a present and asked her what she would like. She eventually settled on some material so she could make herself a new dress. She chose an emerald green worsted and I was pleased with her choice of colour as it would go well with her auburn hair and hazel eyes. This was the first time in her life she had ever had new material. She said she always had hand-me-downs from her mother and aunts. She was thrilled.

It was market day in Thurles and the town was filled with visiting country folk. We mingled with the crowds and browsed in the shop windows. We decided to get something to eat before returning home. We found a small pub which was crowded with visitors. We pushed our way in and found a seat at the window. Mary had never been in a pub before and I could see she was amazed by everything. We ate a quick meal before making our way back to our donkey.

Before hitching the donkey to the cart, I took him to a water trough so he could drink. We also gave him a carrot which we had bought for him in the market.

On the way home, Mary chatted away about everything we'd seen. The visit had been an eye-opener for her as she had never visited a big town before, nor had she seen so many people and so many shops. She was interested to know what I thought about Tom's plans for the school. I told her I wasn't surprised – Tom wasn't getting any younger and it would be good for him to have the support from the Rice Brothers. Both he and Edmund believed education had to be based on religious instruction so it wasn't surprising they were planning to organise their school around a religious brotherhood.

"When I was at school in Thurles, I always thought too much time was spent on religious instruction. That's why I've restricted it to only half an hour each day in the barn." Mary was very impressed with Tom and she was glad she had met him.

We arrived home feeling quite tired. I realised what a toll it must have been on Da when he had ferried me to and from school twice a week. I was glad those days were over but I would never regret them.

Mam was waiting for us in the kitchen with our supper laid out for us. We sat down and whilst we ate, we told her all about our day. Mary showed her the material she had bought. I was slightly uneasy as I couldn't remember Mam ever having a new dress. That evening, I said to Mary, "Next time we're near a draper's shop I must buy some material for Mam." She agreed it was a good idea. We were tired after our long day out so we soon made our way to bed and slept well that night.

We had two more days' 'holiday'. We went to Callan the next day but we didn't stay long as there was little to see there. The town had its share of beggars and the whole place was very run down. I wished we had gone further and visited Kilkenny. In spite of this disappointing visit, we were happy in each other's company. On the third day, I took Mary to visit my cousin David at Ballyduggan.

Ballyduggan is at the foot of Slievenamon. Slievenamon means

'Mountain of the Woman'. As we approached it, I told Mary that at night time it was very spooky on the mountain. It was said to be haunted by people from the 'other world' and according to folklore many of these were women.

We could see the mountain from our home way off in the distance. None of the family had ever climbed it. It looked spectacular on the day we visited David. There was a small white cloud covering the crest but the rest was a lovely bluish purple and gold colour. These colours reflected the gorse and heather that grew there. It was a fine day and the outline of the mountain was set against a bright blue sky.

David was pleased to see us and asked us in. Immediately, I could see his home lacked a woman's touch. David was just 24 years old, and it was obvious from the state of his house that he no longer had a wife, just a brood of young children. He had inherited the lease of the land and farm buildings when his father died. David had other siblings but the girls were married and lived away and his brothers had emigrated, some to America and some to Australia.

As a farmer, David spent many hours out in the fields and little time at home. He took us to show us his land. He had about 20 acres to tend and it was obvious that they were more important to him than the house. He had sheep and cattle in the fields and he kept a pig in the pigsty. He also kept chickens. We were surprised to see the extent of his land. He told us he was negotiating for another strip of land which had recently become vacant and adjoined his at Kylaglass which was nearly 40 acres. He had great plans.

David's children were not at home when we visited. They spent most of their time with a neighbour when David was busy on the farm.

I admired David. He had taken over the farm from his father and it was much improved since he'd been in charge. He worked hard for seven days a week and said that coming to our wedding had been the only day off he'd had in years. Before we left, we promised to keep in touch.

On the way home, Mary said she was sad for David's young children who had lost their mother. We both wondered if he would marry again. It would be good for the children if they had a new mother. We thought it would be good for David too if he had someone to look after him.

CHAPTER TWELVE

Life soon returned to normal after our wedding. The day after our visit to David, Mary was keen to visit her family and see how they were getting on. She set off and I waved her good-bye, then I went to help Da in the fields.

The school was now closed for the holidays and I intended to help Da as much as I could. I was forever grateful to him. He charged us nothing for our keep and he didn't charge rent on the barn. These arrangements were a great help to me, particularly in the early days. My financial position worried me sometimes. My school would never make much money but I was content in the knowledge that I was giving youngsters a good start in life.

If my pupils' parents couldn't afford to pay a fee for schooling, I waived the charge. The normal fee was £2 a quarter. Parents who didn't pay this brought gifts in lieu of payment. These gifts varied from eggs, apples, bread and even potatoes all of which Mam gratefully received. To some extent they helped me repay my parents for their kindness. We always ended up with more food than we needed so Mam took the surplus to church for the poor of the parish.

When Mary came home that day, I was surprised but glad to hear her father had coped well in her absence.

"I'll have to pop back about once a week to help out. Pa has arranged for one of the women in the village to go in twice a week to help. She's even cooking for him. My brothers and sisters are all helping with the laundry and my eldest sister has taken over the sewing. There's plenty to keep them all busy."

"Wonderful! I was worried you would find the house in turmoil and I would be losing you seven days a week!"

"You've no need to worry, Rich. My sister Alice is learning fast. From time to time, I'll show her more. For now, though, everything is in order. In a year or two my visits will be rare, perhaps just once a month. I'm glad to say father seems happy with the new arrangements."

In our spare time, I continued to teach Mary to read and write. She was a quick learner and I hoped it wouldn't be long before she was able to read short stories to the younger children. All in all, things were working out well.

We returned to the barn at the end of the holidays for the new school term. I was pleased to see all my former pupils back with us. We also had six new faces and two of these were girls. We now had so many pupils, I had to split the children into groups – the beginners and the improvers. With two groups to look after I sometimes found it difficult to control them. As soon as my back was turned, someone was up to no good. There was no prospect of finding a helper so I soldiered on as best I could. Even if I did find someone, I couldn't afford to pay him.

One morning, Mary came down to the barn. As she entered, the noise abated. I was surprised to see her so early. She told me she had come to see what all the noise was about. I explained to her how difficult it was to look after two groups at the same time.

"It's hard to teach properly under these circumstances. Things will have to change. But I don't know how. I expect I'll think of something."

When we were relaxing that evening, Mary said to me. "Rich, why don't you let me help you in school? I can look after the young ones for you and try to keep them quiet. It won't be long before I'll be able to read to them. In the meantime, there must be something I can do to help."

So it was that Mary came to the barn twice a day and took the youngsters out for a walk. It was good for them to get fresh air. As they walked, they talked about the plants, the flowers and the animals. The children always returned fresh and keen to get on with their lessons and I was able to concentrate on the older children while they were out.

It wasn't long before Mary was spending more time with us in the school. She started a needlework class for the girls. She usually arrived in the barn around ten o'clock when she had finished helping Mam at home.

One day, in September 1815, she didn't turn up and I was worried. I wanted to go back to the house to see what the problem was but I couldn't leave the children on their own. At lunchtime, the children were outside in the sun, sitting around and eating their lunch, so I rushed home. I was met on the back doorstep by Mam.

"Don't you go worrying yourself now, she's all right. Just a bout of sickness."

I went in and found Mary on the bed upstairs.

"I'm sorry, Rich," she said. "I just couldn't make it. I'm feeling so sick."

I gave her a kiss on her forehead and said, "Don't worry, now. Have you actually been sick?"

"No, Rich, it's just an awful sick feeling in the pit of my stomach. I keep retching but nothing comes up. It seems to take all my energy away. I've never been like this before. I've not been ill since I was little. Whatever can be wrong with me?"

I told her to rest, and try and sleep. I went downstairs and talked to Mam. I asked her if she knew what it might be. She smiled at me.

"I think I know – she might be pregnant. Some women suffer with sickness in the mornings in the early months of pregnancy. You mustn't worry."

I was amazed! We had talked about having children but I didn't think it would happen this quickly.

I rushed back upstairs to see Mary again.

"Mary, my love, have you no idea what's causing this?" She looked surprised at my question. I told her Mam thought she might be pregnant. Although she felt ill, she was delighted and we both hugged each other and laughed. Nothing could have felt better!

"Have you missed your 'time'?" She replied she thought she might have but only a short while ago. We decided that if she was pregnant, it could only be the early stages, maybe only six weeks.

"So, I'm not ill," she said. "It's just a symptom. I think I'll get up now."

Mary came downstairs and said that now she knew the reason for feeling unwell she was much happier. Mam told her she must take care as miscarriages were common in the first few months of pregnancy and she told her not to do any heavy lifting or strenuous activity.

The morning sickness didn't last long. After six weeks, Mary was looking bonny and healthy. We prayed all would go well over the next few months. She continued to help me with the younger children and I was amazed at how quickly she had learned to read and write. She was now teaching the younger children the alphabet. I sometimes wondered how I would manage when she was confined and later on when she had a baby to look after. I decided to meet that problem when it came.

At that time, Da seemed to spend half his time in his workshop making his barrels and the other half out in the fields. During the summer holidays I helped as much as I could on the farm.

It was harvest time again, a time when Da always needed help. We had had a good year and it looked as if we would have the best harvest for years. As usual, we started early on a bright sunny morning, praying the good weather would continue. Uncle Thomas and a couple of lads from the village were helping us.

Mam and Mary arrived at midday, carrying our lunch. Mam said it was like feeding the five thousand. She had brought enough bread and cheese for everyone. Uncle Thomas went home to collect the cider barrel and mugs.

Everyone said how bonny Mary was looking. She now had only two months to go before the birth. Mam had arranged for the local handywoman, Joan Sullivan, to come and assist with the birth. Joan had helped with all the births in our family and she had been working for families in the district for nearly 30 years. Everyone in our neighbourhood called on her to help with birthing; she could be relied on to do a good job. She was always busy, helping not only with births, but also with all sorts of accidents and illnesses.

Joan fulfilled a vital role in our community. It took a long time to get a message to our doctor in Ballingarry as he was a few miles away. He was also very expensive. Joan wasn't medically trained and she always referred a patient to the doctor if a problem was beyond her capability.

The day came when Mary went into labour. She complained to Mam of pains and Mam sent straight away for Joan. She arrived two hours later when Mary's waters had just broken. I sat anxiously downstairs in the kitchen waiting for news. A few uneasy hours went by. I heard Mary crying out in pain; it seemed to go on for hours. I had never been more nervous. The wait was unbearable. Later, from upstairs, I heard the sound of a baby crying. Mam appeared with a big smile on her face and called down, "Richard, you have a baby daughter!" I started to climb the stairs.

"Can I see them?"

"Wait a while," Mam replied. "Give Joan ten minutes to clear up."

It was the longest ten minutes of my life!

I was amazed when I saw our little girl. She was sleeping peacefully in Mary's arms.

"I think she's going to be a contented one," said Joan.

I gave Mary a kiss and said, "Well done."

The next day, we took our little one – our first child – to the priest to be christened. We named her Catherine after my grandmother in Carrick. When we arrived home after the ceremony, we found the house full of well-wishers. People were always looking for an excuse to get together and celebrate, and this was one of them.

Life soon returned to normal. Mary was still able to help me in the barn. Whenever baby Catherine was asleep, she popped down and spent an hour or two with the youngsters while Mam was left in charge of the baby. Little Catherine was a very happy little thing and she was no trouble to Mam. As Joan had said, she was a contented one.

On the last day of October, we celebrated Halloween. This was the first time we had partied at that time of the year as we didn't believe the old superstitions about the ghosts of the dead returning to earth that day. Celebrating the day was an old Celtic tradition. We invited our neighbours to join us and it was a very festive gathering. We lit a large bonfire in the field to ward off the 'the evil spirits' which some people believed would visit us that night. One of the neighbours dressed up as a witch and told everyone's fortunes. Mam had made barmbrack for us and we sat eating and drinking around the fire.

All the spooky decorations had to be removed by midnight as the following day was All Saints Day. In place of them, we decorated the house with greenery and flags. I looked forward to the future when we would have young children who would enjoy this celebration with us. Halloween was a sign that winter was fast approaching, and dark evenings and cold nights would soon be with us.

The years passed by and we had three more children. John was born in 1817 and named after my grandfather. Richard was born in 1820, Thomas in 1822, and eight years later, in 1830, our last son, Michael, was born.

¤

During the last few years efforts had been made by the government to make all leaseholders pay a tax on the agricultural land they held. My cousin David was amongst many who were very vocal in their opposition to this tax. Our main objection was that it would be paid to support the Church of Ireland. Like many, we thought this unfair; we already supported the Catholic Church. This was another effort by the government to impoverish Catholics. Many of our neighbours were annoyed by this tax but there was little we could do to stop it. We waited for the arrival of the surveyors who would measure our land and put us on the list of taxpayers. No one was happy.

¤

Over the years, I continued to stay in touch with my teacher, Tom Cahill, in Thurles. Tom and his brother William had paid several visits to Edmund Rice in Waterford and they became more involved with the Presentation Brothers. Eventually, in 1822, they went to Waterford and took their vows as religious Brothers in the Presentation Brotherhood. They returned to Thurles where Tom continued to run their school but this time as a monastery of the Presentation Brothers. Tom was director of the monastery and involved with the welfare of the boys while his brother William was the head teacher, helped by two young trainee teachers. The number of pupils in the school had swollen to well over one hundred and had been split into three classes – juniors, a middle school and seniors. A true success story.

Mary asked me if I was interested in getting involved with the Edmund Rice movement. The schools were opening in other districts apart from Thurles and Waterford and were all successful. I was quick to tell her that nothing was further from my mind. My main object as a teacher was to make my pupils fit for life and I thought these schools spent far too much time on religious instruction. I didn't want to increase the half hour we spent on religion each day. Many changes would have to be made if we joined the Rice Brotherhood. I respected its aims but I didn't want to be involved.

CHAPTER THIRTEEN

One person who visited us regularly at Islands was Scan the tinker. He came again in August 1822 one day when we were all in the kitchen. We heard a knock on the back door and in walked Sean, saying, as he always did, "God bless all here." To which we responded, "God bless you too."

He settled down at the kitchen table and told us about the failure of the potato crop in the north west of Ireland. Potatoes were the staple diet for many in our country and the poor ate nothing else. As a result of the crop failure, many people were dying of starvation. We were lucky that the blight had not reached us in the south.

Our family was fortunate that we didn't rely on potatoes for our main source of food as many others did. We had a varied diet – we kept a pig and chickens. The pig provided us with bacon and the chickens with eggs. We also had a cow which provided us with milk. If we were careful our farm provided us with enough food to sustain us but if the worst came to the worst, we had enough land to expand the farm and grow more crops. Da had suggested opening up the fields which had lain barren as we could grow barley and oats there. There was also the possibility of keeping more cattle. Da's ideas were good but I didn't think he would be able to cope with the extra work on top of his coopering business. Help would have to come from somewhere else. He had grand ideas but at that moment it looked as if these would not be fulfilled.

We all looked forward to pig killing day. When our pig was

fattened, a man came from Mullinahone to help with the killing. Da and the man tied a rope round the pig and dragged him out of the stye. The pig was hung up at the entrance to the barn by its hind legs. There was a lot of squawking and squealing. The girls in the family ran inside when this was about to happen as they couldn't bear to watch it but the boys always stayed around to watch the action. As quickly as possible, the man thrust his knife through the pig's heart. The squealing soon stopped as the poor animal died. Da collected the blood by placing a bowl underneath. He added salt to the blood so it wouldn't thicken. Mam came out with a bowl of breadcrumbs and these were thrown into the mixture. She took the bowl away into the kitchen where she made sausages and black pudding which we would all enjoy over the next few days.

The pieces of pork which were surplus to our needs were taken away by the man. He sold them for us at market. We kept the best pieces of meat and these were salted for our own use.

As young boys, we couldn't wait for pig killing days. We had a competition to see which one of us could persuade Da to let us have the pig's bladder. This was a trophy! When we had cleaned it, we blew it up and tied the neck and used it as a football. It made us very popular with local lads who all came into our field to have a kickabout. Those were good days.

After Da had salted the pork, it was hung up in the woodshed to cure. Mam made soups and stews from the hocks and we had a good supply of salted bacon for the future. We all loved a meal of cabbage, bacon and potatoes. Soon after the killing, Da would buy a baby piglet to replace the one that we had lost. Then the fattening process would start all over again.

Very occasionally, Mam would wring a chicken's neck and cook it for us. She had no compunction about killing hens. I couldn't watch her doing this but Uncle Thomas always took great interest in it. He came in, laughing, and said to me, "You should have seen it! After your Ma had wrung its neck, it refused to die and ran around in circles with its poor head on one side. Then it fell to the ground and passed out." I couldn't laugh at this with my uncle. I thought it was cruel. But even so we enjoyed a meal of roast chicken. The day after was even better when we had cold chicken with tatties.

We didn't eat meat every day but on weekends we always had hearty meals. One of our favourites was lamb stew. When Lent came, meat was not eaten for forty days. After Lent, we looked forward to Easter when we could start eating meat again. In future, if our potato crop failed, we knew we had other food to fall back on.

The failure of the potato crop in the north of the country was caused by a blight which killed off the plants. When people went to dig up their crop, all they found was black, slimy rotting roots and no potatoes. We had a long talk about this and hoped the potato blight wouldn't reach us. Mam said if our potato crop failed, the alternative to potatoes was bread. We had plenty of wheat flour in store which would see us through several months. Da said if our crops failed, we would have to eat smaller portions than usual. We hoped everything would be all right for us but we were sorry for those poor people who had nothing to fall back on.

That year the potato blight didn't come our way but we kept our eyes open for it in future. In fact, it was about 20 years before the blight came again.

¤

Our first two children, Catherine and John, were now both attending school in the barn. Both were bright and learned their lessons quickly. I often wondered what the future would hold for them. I hoped, in my heart of hearts, that the laws would change and eventually they would be able to use their learning in their future lives. I prepared them well for the future but I couldn't be certain what this would be.

Even though we were well set up at the school, I couldn't get it out of my mind that we were 'illegal'. Technically, we were not a hedge school as we operated indoors. People still called illegal schools 'hedge schools' and called the teachers 'teachers of the hedge'. We had to be careful. If we put a foot wrong, we could easily be closed down. But the authorities turned a blind eye to us as long as we were not causing any trouble.

¤

There had always been confusion in the family over names. The naming tradition in Ireland is followed by most families: the first son was always named after his grandfather and the first daughter after her grandmother and so on.

We tried to overcome this mix-up by shortening names: Catherine became Kate and John became Jack in the hope they would not be confused with others in the family. In due course, all our children had nicknames. Richard was Dick so as not to be muddled with me, Thomas was Tom, and Michael was Mikey.

We were a very close family. There were three generations living in our house, though this was not unusual in Ireland. One evening, we were all sitting round the fire in the kitchen and I told our children about their great-grandparents who lived in Carrick-on-Suir, way down in the south of the county. They were intrigued as they had never met them and didn't know of their existence until then. They asked lots of questions. I told them all I knew and said that one day we might all be able to visit them.

CHAPTER FOURTEEN

We were not a family with any particular political persuasion. We led busy lives and we didn't have time to get involved in politics. Recently, however, we had thought it important to keep in touch with the political situation in the country as more and more people were agitating for the Penal Laws to be finally removed. In 1823, a prominent lawyer called Daniel O'Connell set up the Catholic Association. The aims of the Association were being spread by Catholic priests, who were encouraging their flocks to join the movement. The purpose of it was to fight for Home Rule and for Catholic Emancipation. Da and I had long discussions as to whether or not we should join the Association. If the movement was strong enough to achieve its stated aims, we were all for it. However, we didn't join immediately but kept abreast of local feeling.

Eventually, like many Irish Catholics, we joined. There was a long queue of people at church who, like us, were waiting to sign up to the Association. We had decided that we had very little to lose but if the movement was successful, we had a lot to gain. The ambitions of the Association were being spread by Catholic priests who were keen to enrol as many of their congregation as possible into the movement. We paid a fee of one penny a month which would help fund the Association's aims and was collected at church after Mass.

In 1825, the Catholic Association was declared illegal by the authorities who were irritated by the continued agitation the Association was causing. But Daniel O'Connell was not worried. He was a lawyer and knew how to circumvent the law. He just changed the name of the Association and it continued to operate.

The agitation of the Association continued for a few more years until 1929 when, at last, the Irish Emancipation Act was passed by the British government. This paved the way for Catholics to be able to worship in their own churches and for our children to be educated in proper schools. It was to have a far-reaching impact on our future lives. It would be many more years before we were entirely free but it was a big step in the right direction. I hoped we would now see an alteration in our lives, although I doubted if I would see many changes in my lifetime. Our children would hopefully be the ones to benefit.

With the passing of the Act, we could at last start to think ahead to the future. Did the changes in the law mean we would have official schools which our children could attend? Did it mean we could worship in our churches without fearing the long arm of the law? After long years of suppression, it was difficult to believe it could be true. This Act brought a mood of optimism to the country.

We soon heard about new schools which had already been set up in other parts of the country. In 1827 in the Midlands, in a town called Durrow, two schools had been opened in anticipation of the new Act. One was run in a stable and catered for Catholic boys and girls. The other was in a thatched mud cabin. No effort was made to keep these schools secret. They were allowed to continue with no interference from the law. Progress was promising but slow. I hoped the day might come when my school might be officially recognised. A year later, in 1828, we heard of another school set up in Killenaule which was only about 15 miles west of us. We began to see a light at the end of the tunnel.

Another promising event in 1828 was the laying of the foundation stone for the new Catholic church in Ballingarry. There was great excitement. We wondered how long it would be before our new church was completed. Work started quite soon but it was two or three years before we were able to worship in the finished building.

There had not been so much excitement for years. It's difficult to describe what this meant to us. Having been forbidden to worship as Catholics for so many years, we would now be able to do this in our own new church without fear of the law. It was very exciting!

But things were not so good everywhere. There were still many people suffering. People knew that the Penal Laws had been revoked but it seemed to make little difference to their lives. They couldn't see a future for themselves and many of them were desperate either for a roof over their heads or for food. Desperation led to troubles in many parts of the country.

ᴖ

I now had 35 pupils in my school. Twenty-four of these were boys and the rest girls. Many parents still couldn't see the importance of girls having an education. But things were gradually starting to change. I could see a time in the future when boys and girls were treated equally. I wondered how long it would be before we saw this improvement in our lives.

ᴖ

Lately, I had noticed Da was finding it difficult to cope on the farm and run his cooperage business. Looking after both seemed to be wearing him down. He regularly complained of aches and pains in his knees and legs – not a good sign. We racked our brains to see how we could help on the farm as we wanted to relieve Da of this responsibility and leave him free to concentrate on coopering.

Jack was now nearly 14 and had progressed well at school. There wasn't much more I could teach him so I wondered if I should let him leave school and work for Da. As the eldest son, Jack might eventually take over the farm. I thought it would be good if he could get an early start. He had shown a keen interest in the farm from an early age. I talked to Mary and she agreed that he was suited to work on the land. We decided to talk to Da about him leaving school and working for him.

One day, I took John aside and said I wanted to have a talk with him. He looked worried and said, "What is it, Pa, have I done something wrong?"

"No, nothing like that. In fact, I'm very pleased with the way you've worked at school. But the time has come for you to decide what you would like to do in future. You're a lucky boy as Granpa has suggested that if you leave school, you might like to work on the farm with him. What do you think of that?"

"Oh, Pa! That's a great idea. Can I leave school straight away? I'm getting bored with it now. You know how much I like working with Granpa."

"Well, there's no time like the present. You've worked with Granpa many times in the school holidays so I know you're suited to the work. Granpa's not getting any younger and he needs help. In fact, if you like, you can start from next week."

Jack was very excited. He couldn't wait to tell his friends the news. It wasn't long before he was up at 5 o'clock every day, before everyone else, and out in the fields either milking the cow or collecting eggs from the chickens or doing a thousand other jobs.

Our second son, young Dick, was turning out to be a star pupil. He was far ahead of children his own age and had a very inquisitive mind. He had a tendency to spend time reading the Bible which was unusual for a boy of his age and he was especially attentive in religious lessons. I speculated that maybe one day he might want to be a priest. At the age of ten, it was too soon to tell where his life would lead. I wondered about this. He was not suited to work in the fields or with animals like Jack and sometimes I wondered if the Thurles school would be good for him. He would enjoy their religious classes and mixing with other boys would be good for him.

¤

But back to the farm. David Frisby, my cousin, reminded me about the tithe plot listings. The government would soon be sending surveyors all over the country to make detailed lists of all agricultural holdings. These lists would contain the names of leaseholders, a description of their property, and the acreage they held. The purpose of the lists was to enable the government to charge a tithe or tax on all agricultural land holdings. This tax would be 10% of the value of productive agricultural land and it would be paid to the Church of Ireland. There were murmurings of discontent in the farming community.

The land surveyor came one day and spoke to Da. He went out and measured our land and noted down details of our house. He also listed all the outbuildings.

I joined him and Da outside. I wanted to be with them to make sure all was in order. Very little of our land was productive agricultural land and I pointed this out to the surveyor. The tax was only meant to be charged on 'productive' land. I told him Da spent the majority of his time working in his workshop as a cooper and shouldn't be classified as a farmer. The surveyor made a note of this, but not before asking if we had any other help on the farm. We hoped that when he saw how busy Da was in his workshop, he might reduce the amount of tithe we would have to pay. It would be some time before we heard the result of his visit.

Soon the tithe would have to be paid. We were still unhappy that the tax would be used to support the clergy in the Church of Ireland. We already paid towards the support of the Catholic priests. It seemed very unfair. We didn't want to support the Protestant clergy. Many people were against the tax and said they would refuse to pay it.

CHAPTER FIFTEEN

One evening, I sat with Da, Mam and Mary in the kitchen and we discussed our children. Jack was well established working on the farm for Granpa and we wondered if Kate would soon be leaving school like Jack. She was a great help to Mam around the house and she loved to sew and cook. She didn't have any boyfriends and we thought it would be some time before she married. Mam was glad to have her help in the school holidays. Mary and I wondered if we could find some other interest for her. Could we find somewhere where she could meet up with boys and girls of her own age? It was very difficult as we lived so far away from the towns.

Only two weeks later, we noticed Kate had become friendly with one of the boys in school. His name was Brendan Molloy and he lived with his parents near Ballingarry. His father was a boot and shoe maker. I had often taken my boots to him when they needed repairing. We were pleased with this development and wondered if it would come to anything.

"Don't expect anything. This is only her first boyfriend. She'll probably have many more before she gets married," I said to Mary.

"Well, you and I never had anybody else before we got hitched!" she said.

We laughed.

"Yes, I agree," I said, "but I think it's too soon for her. Brendan is a good chap and she couldn't do better! I know we both want to see her happily settled. Let's wait a while and see how this friendship progresses."

¤

Da was glad to have Jack helping him on the farm. He said he was a natural and it wouldn't be long before he could be left alone to look after things and Da could continue with his coopering uninterrupted. Uncle Thomas and his son George still helped Da in the workshop and, when necessary, they did odd jobs around the farm. George, my cousin, was a friendly chap and very gregarious. He wasn't needed every day in the workshop. When he wasn't working for Da or Jack, he would wander off to neighbouring farms to find more work. He was very popular in the locality and never had trouble in finding other work.

¤

One evening we talked about the possibility of sending young Dick to school in Thurles. I was convinced it would be good for him. He wasn't suited to work on the land so this extra schooling could be a good foundation for his future life. Mary knew that I often thought about what he would do after school. She told me I shouldn't plan our children's future lives for them. In due time they would all know what they wanted to do. She said we shouldn't push them in a direction which might be wrong for them.

"I know you sometimes wonder if Dick will become a priest. If Dick wants to go into the Church, he'll find his own way there."

I was surprised at Mary's outburst. She was normally in agreement with everything I said.

"Well," I said, "to a certain extent I agree with you but, look at Jack – he's found his feet on the farm. He didn't have to be pushed into it." Mary agreed and remarked that the other children were not like Jack. It might not be so easy to find employment for them.

We returned to the discussion about Dick going away to school in Thurles. Da asked me how I would get him there. I said he would have to be a boarder as I had been and he would only come home for the holidays. We all agreed it was probably the best thing for him. In due course I would give it more thought.

Young Thomas, our third son, was now eight and he was the quietest one in the family. He attended his lessons regularly but he was certainly not a bright spark and he was too young for us to start planning his future.

Mary had her hands full with our latest addition to the family, young Mikey. He was only a few months old but Mary still had time to help me at school. Mam looked after Mikey when Mary was helping me. Mam loved babies and caring for young Mikey was a joy for her. She was glad every day when Mary made her way to the barn and she was left alone with him.

One day, I took Dick aside and asked him what he wanted to do when he eventually left school. He looked nonplussed and had obviously never thought about it. It was a silly question I suppose as he was not yet old enough to think about this. I told him I was pleased with his progress at school and asked him if he would like to go away to school in Thurles. He knew I had been educated there.

"Jack didn't go away to school, why me?" he replied.

I explained to him he could study a large range of subjects which I was unable to teach him. He was very apprehensive about the whole idea.

"If you do decide to go, Dick, it will be expensive for me so I am only suggesting this as I think it will be good for you. I know you would like the school as it gives more time to religious studies than I do. I know you'd like that."

A smile appeared on his face; I could see he might be changing his mind.

"Hmm! It sounds all right."

I told him to think about it and not to rush into a decision. I could see he was already half-way to making up his mind. We were nearly at the end of the summer term so there was plenty of time for him to agree. The summer holidays lay ahead of us. If he decided it was for him, we would have to contact the school well before the start of the autumn term.

I was surprised when, in just a few days' time, Dick came see me.

"Da, I have been thinking of your suggestion and I think I would like to go to school in Thurles."

A couple of weeks later, we were on our way to the school. I had written ahead to Tom Cahill, telling him we would be visiting. I told Dick that Mr. Cahill, the head, would want to interview him. We drove along the country lanes and were deep in conversation most of the way. It was a lovely day. The birds were singing in the hedgerows and numerous wild flowers were blooming along the sides of the lanes. Dick was very keen now to change schools but I warned him he could only go if there was a place for him. We would find that out in the next few hours.

Tom Cahill greeted us on the front doorstep of the school.

"So, this is Dick, is it? He looks just like you, Richard, when you first came here." After shaking hands, he said, "Come on in, both of you."

We spent nearly three hours at the school. Tom interviewed Dick for nearly half an hour and afterwards he took us on a tour of the school. Then he said to Dick, "After all you've seen and heard, Richard, are you interested in joining us?"

Dick beamed. "Yes, sir, there is nothing I would like more."

"I'll write to you in the next few days and let you know if we can offer you a place."

After saying goodbye to Tom, we picked up some shopping for Mam in the town and then made our way home. Dick chatted to me all the way home and I knew we had made the right decision for him. I hadn't seen him so enthused for a long time.

¤

When we arrived home, Mary met us at the front gate.

"Richard, we've had some bad news. Come inside and I'll tell you about it."

I left Dick to put the donkey and cart away and hurried inside.

"Whatever's happened?" I asked.

Indoors, Da and Mam were in the kitchen, looking very unhappy. At midday, a messenger had arrived on horseback and had given Da a piece of paper which he now handed to me. I read it aloud. *Sorry to advise you your mother Eleanor passed away last night. From your father John Frisby.* I sat down in shock.

"Da, I'm so sorry. Did the messenger give you any further information?" Da replied that all the messenger had was the note. He couldn't tell us any more.

It was several years since I'd seen my grandparents. I was only a young boy when we moved to Islands and we had left Gran and Gramps behind in Carrick-on-Suir. Gramps was still working at his cooperage when we left but had retired a year or two ago. Many memories of them flooded through my mind. Even though I was young when we left Carrick, I still remembered them well from our time living with them in their tiny cottage.

All was quiet in the kitchen.

"Richard," Da said to me, "we'll have to go to the funeral! The messenger stayed and had a meal with us at midday and I sent him back with a reply. *Very sorry to hear your news. We'll be with you soon."*

All was very quiet and Mary made herself busy at the fireside, stirring the pot which contained our evening meal. We all started talking at once. I offered to go with Da. It was now the school holidays and I had plenty of free time.

I wanted to support Da. Mam and Mary decided to stay at home. They both thought Da and I should go on our own. Even if they had wanted to come with us, there was no room for them in the cart.

Da said he would leave Uncle Thomas in charge of his workshop. He wasn't worried about the farm as Jack was in full control now and would take care of that.

The next morning, we were up early and on our way to Carrick. Fortunately, the weather was good. The donkey was tired after his trip to Thurles the previous day but donkeys are workhorses and, provided we stopped and watered him occasionally, we knew he would make the journey. We didn't expect to be back the same day and said we might be away for a couple of nights, it all depended on the timing of the funeral.

Da was of course shocked by the news. He regretted he hadn't seen his mother for several months. He was very quiet on the journey. I thought it was best not to talk too much. I left him to his sad thoughts. It took us six hours to get to Carrick. I had no idea where my grandparents lived but Da drove straight there without a problem.

As I had only lived in Carrick up to the age of four, my memories were scant. My earliest memories of Gran and Gramps were when all the family were together on Christmas Day. Gran was a lovely little lady with a round face and she was always smiling. Now she was gone. Although Da had been back a few times over the years to see his parents, Mam had never gone with him. She had never returned to Carrick and had never been back to visit her own family.

When we arrived at the cottage, all was in darkness. Da went in through the back door which was open. I put the donkey in the field and put the cart away. I followed Da in and we found Gramps in the kitchen, sitting all alone. It was dusk when we arrived so we lit some candles and I lit the fire which had gone out. As soon as I had the fire going, I went out to the pump for water. I left Da and Gramps alone so they could talk about their loss.

When I returned with the water, Da and Gramps had gone to see Granma who was laid out in the bedroom. Apparently, several neighbours had helped him. They had dressed her in her Sunday best and two of them were still sitting with her, one on either side of the bed, and praying with their rosaries. They had lit candles at each side of the bed.

The fire was now going well and I looked around for food. The cupboards were empty so I went out to find a shop. I was lucky to find one still open and I bought bread and eggs, cheese and milk. It was strange doing this as we baked our own bread at home, our chickens laid eggs for us and our cow provided us with milk. If we had known what state we would find Gramps in, Mam would have made up a basket of food for us. It had all been such a rush. She probably thought about it after we left.

When I returned to the cottage, I set about making a meal for us. It wasn't much but Gramps tucked into his hungrily. He hadn't eaten for a day or two.

¤

Now Grandma had died Gramps was a poor lost soul. They had just lived for each other and he couldn't imagine life without her.

The funeral had been arranged for the next day and I was glad the priest had visited and taken it all in hand before our arrival. I thought it would be a small gathering and wondered what, if any, arrangements had been made for the wake. When we finished eating, the neighbours who had been sitting with Granma decided it was time to go home to their families. Before they went, I thanked them and asked them if any arrangements had been made for the wake. They said it was all arranged and several neighbours had got together to provide the food and drink. I was relieved and we thanked them, bid them goodnight and waved them off at the back door.

After they left, Gramps told us how good they had been to him.

"But I couldn't stand those banshees. They came yesterday, keening away, making a horrible noise. I told them to go away. Granma wouldn't have liked it. They went away with their tails between their legs!"

Da laughed and said, "They'll probably curse us now!"

Gramps lived in a small cottage. I asked him if he had slept the previous night and he said he didn't want to go to bed with Granma lying there so he'd slept in the chair in the kitchen. There was another small room next to the kitchen which was rarely used. Da told me that he and Mam had slept there from the first day of their marriage and I had been born there. It was now used as a small parlour. Da and I decided to sleep on the floor in that room. It wasn't going to be a comfortable night on the cold floor but we had no other choice.

We only had rush matting beneath us. We covered ourselves with rugs and coats. Eventually, I heard Da snoring and I was glad he was asleep. It had been a long and emotional day for him. I wondered if I would sleep at all but I was tired too and soon followed him into the land of nod.

The following morning, I found some oats in the cupboard and made a stirabout for our breakfast. I talked to Gramps about the funeral. He said he wasn't looking forward to it. After breakfast, I fetched more water from the pump so we could wash before the service. We had worn our Sunday best for the journey but it had become very creased and untidy. It would have to do.

At 12 o'clock, there was a knock at the back door and two young men appeared.

They were neighbours and they were delivering a coffin. I was surprised and asked them where it had come from. They said the neighbours had knocked it together. They knew Gramps couldn't afford an undertaker so they had taken it on themselves to help. I thanked them and asked them in.

I said, "How are we going to do this?"

"My mam is coming soon with the handywoman," one of them replied, "and they will organise everything. Mam knows what to do. She's done it before. When they've put her in the box, we'll be here to nail the lid down."

It was all very strange but Da and I were glad these good neighbours were helping us.

Shortly after noon, the coffin was placed on a cart and the banshees arrived again, chanting their woeful tunes. Their keening was a horrible sound and Da told them they weren't wanted.

"Go away! We told you yesterday we didn't want you."

One of the neighbours turned to me and said, "He's done it now. Those old banshees will put a curse on him. Look at them all gossiping together. They're not used to treatment like that!"

We laughed together as we watched them go. We didn't believe in curses. Just before one o'clock, we all made our way in procession to the ruined church which still served as a place of worship.

I thanked God the weather was good. The priest was waiting for us and I was surprised that so many people had turned up. I didn't know any of them but Da recognised many and occasionally tipped his hat to them.

The funeral service was short and Granma was soon committed to the grave. I shed a tear as the sods of earth followed her coffin down into the depths. I crossed myself and thanked God all had gone smoothly.

Afterwards, we stood around for a while. Many people wanted to talk to Da and offer their condolences. I stood beside him, listening to the memories they were recalling of Granma. She had been well loved by her neighbours and they wanted to give her a good send-off.

As people drifted away, we made our way back to the cottage where the wake had already started. The neighbours had come in to prepare the food and drink and I could tell Gramps wasn't easy with so many people in his cottage, but this was the custom. A wake was always held to remember the best things about the person who had died and to celebrate their life. I always thought this was a strange time for rejoicing. The neighbours had been good to Granma and Gramps over the years and we had no option but to join in. After a few drinks, the singing began. To the tune of the fiddler and the piper, all the old folk tunes were sung. In spite of the merriment, I found it all very sad.

Da knew most of the neighbours. Whenever I looked over at him, he was always deep in conversation. These were the people he had grown up with.

One or two of the ladies came over and chatted with me. They told me Gramps had been quite an important person in Carrick. Like Da, he had been a cooper but he ran a larger concern, employing ten people. He was well liked and it was thought to be an honour to work for him. Another lady, whose name was Maggie, said she had made baskets for Gramps. She said she arrived at the works early every morning to pick up the reeds and take them home. Like most of the women workers, she worked at home. She said it was an easy job but hard on the hands and she showed me the callouses on her fingers. Even wearing gloves was no protection. Her husband Jim told me he used to take the finished baskets down to the river for Gramps. I asked why he took them there.

"Sure," he said, "they sent them down river to Waterford. Your grandpappy sold them there. We couldn't make enough of them. There was always a great demand for them. A distant relative of yours sold them at the Waterford fair."

It was good for me to hear these tales about my grandparents as Da had never talked to us about his home life. I was proud to be their grandson.

After a few hours, people drifted away. We were all tired and decided to go to bed early. I was dreading another night on the stone floor but it was far too late to go home. Our journey back would have to wait until next day

Before settling down for the night, Gramps thanked us for coming. He said he couldn't have gone through it on his own. He was glad we had been there to support him.

"Will you write to your brothers in America for me?" he asked Da. "They will be sad to hear the news."

Da had two brothers in America but he rarely talked about them. They had emigrated so many years ago that most people had forgotten about them.

I noticed Gramps kept talking about his son, Patrick. He was sorry he had not been there for his mother's funeral. I had never heard of Patrick before so later I asked Da who he was. I discovered that Patrick was the eldest son in the family and he had emigrated to Newfoundland many years ago, long before his other brothers went to America. Apparently, my grandparents were devastated when he left home. Da remembered the occasion well. He told me that one morning they'd noticed Patrick wasn't at breakfast and thought he was sleeping in late. But later in the day he still didn't appear. My grandfather asked Da if he had any idea where Patrick was. Da had no idea but said he would ask around. He went down the road to a friend and asked him if he knew. The lad didn't want to tell him as he said everyone would say it was bad news. In the end, the story came out. Patrick had gone with a friend to a ship in Waterford and the ship had sailed to Newfoundland. There was a great need there for men to help in the fishing industry.

Newfoundland was famous for its cod and fishing was the main industry. Da's friend told him many young men from the area had gone there. Most of them stayed for six months during the summer but when winter came, the weather was so bad that there was no possibility of the boats putting out to sea to fish. With nothing to do, some of the lads returned to Ireland with their pockets full of money. Others stayed, married a local girl, and settled down. Da always hoped Patrick would be among the returning lads. He hoped the family would see him back again at the end of that summer. But he never did return.

Da had had the unenviable task of telling his parents what had happened to Patrick. His parents knew nothing about Newfoundland or the fishing industry. It was a great shock to them and difficult for them to understand why Patrick had been so keen to go. Da told them Patrick might return home at the end of the summer. They were very upset that Patrick, their eldest son, had gone away without telling them.

The family never heard from him again.

"We don't know if his ship ever reached Newfoundland and we'll never know what became of him," said Da. The family always wondered if he'd arrived safely and had married and settled down. I wondered why Da had never told us this before. I suppose it was just one of those family stories almost forgotten in the mists of time. It was clearly painful for him to talk about it.

Gramps asked me why Uncle Thomas hadn't come with us. I said I'd offered to give up my seat in the cart to him but he refused, saying he would stay and look after the workshop.

"I'm not surprised," Gramps grunted. There seemed to be some ill feeling there and I wondered what the cause was.

Later, before we went to bed, I asked Da if he was happy about leaving Gramps on his own when we went home. He said he'd been thinking about it and he was going to offer to take him back home with us. We decided to talk to him about it.

So, Da asked Gramps if he had thought about the future – living on his own in the cottage. Gramps mumbled he could manage but Da was not happy about leaving him.

"Sure, you could come back with us. We would be happier if you were with us and not on your own here." For the first time, I saw a semblance of a smile on Gramps' face.

"That's grand of you. Give me some time to think about it."

We talked about Granma and how much she would be missed. I could see tears in Gramps' eyes. They had been together for nearly sixty years and I could only imagine how dreadful the loss must be for him.

The following morning, after a quick stirabout for breakfast, Gramps settled down in his chair. He said he wanted to have a rest before we left him. We had a couple of hours to spare so Da and I went out for a walk around Carrick. Da pointed out all his old haunts to me. He took me down to the River Suir and showed me the remains of the old mud hut where he had attended his hedge school. The hut was in ruins now but for Da it was a reminder of his young life. He pointed out to me the spot on the river where he used to go for a swim.

"We had so much fun in the water. We had races to see who was the strongest swimmer. Those were the days."

He took me to see the old workshop where Gramps had his coopering business. It was a big building and now stood empty. We couldn't go inside as it was locked up. We wandered round the back where there were still signs of the business, piles of wood and large logs. I noticed the willow saplings lying about on the ground.

"Da," I said, "are these of any use to you? They may be good for the baskets."

He walked over towards me and picked one or two up.

"No," he replied. "Look at this one here. It's been out in the rain for too long and is going rotten." He showed me how easily it broke. I thought it was a shame so much raw material was going to waste. Da said the wood wasn't worth much. I looked around and was struck by the desolation of the place. We made our way back to the cottage.

Gramps was up and about when we arrived back. He had made cheese sandwiches for us and we ate these with some beer left over from the previous day. As we sat munching, Gramps said, "I've been thinking about your offer. And, yes, thank you, I would like to come back with you." Da was delighted and they stood up and hugged each other. Gramps went over to the sideboard and took down a mug from the shelf and poured the contents on to the table. We counted it up and it came to £3 and five shillings.

"Here's my next rent," said Gramps. "This is all I have in the world. I was wondering what I would do when it was gone. Here you are, Richard, you have it. It'll pay something towards my keep. I'm afraid that's all I have to give you." Da refused to take the money as he thought his father might find a need for it in the future.

"Keep it," he said. "When I'm short, I can come to you for a loan." We all laughed.

So, it was decided. Gramps was coming to live with us. We hadn't thought about the logistics, such as where he would sleep in our house. Da said Mam would surely know what to do and we would sort it out later. Our immediate problem was how we were all going to ride back to Islands in our cart. There wouldn't be room for three of us as well as Gramps' box of belongings. We had to think of an alternative.

Da said I would have to find my own way home. He thought the Bianconi Mail Coach went from Carrick to Kilkenny which would take me part of the way home. I went out to find the local Bianconi agent. I asked someone to direct me to him and it was not long before I was in his shop. He confirmed there was a mail coach travelling from Carrick to Kilkenny daily.

I asked about the stops on the way. He said the only official stops were Kilmanagh and Kells. But he said if I wanted to get off elsewhere, the driver would stop the coach for me. I thought Kells was probably the best stopping off point for me and I would ask Da to meet me there.

I purchased a ticket for the following day, allowing Da time to get home to Islands before coming to meet me. That meant another night in Carrick for me. The coach would leave just after three o'clock in the afternoon. It was a two-hour journey to Kells so I would arrive at about five o'clock. The fare for the journey was two shillings and nine pence.

When I had sorted out my travel arrangements, I went back to the cottage and helped load the cart with Gramps' belongings. They were soon off and I waved them goodbye. I had nothing to do for the rest of the day as I wasn't leaving until the next day in the afternoon and I wondered what I would do with my time.

When they had gone, I decided to have a good look around the cottage. It was strange without anyone else there. I was struck by the silence. I wondered how Granma and Gramps had managed in these last few years as clearly Gramps was down to his last few shillings. He was a very proud man and I'm sure he wouldn't have asked Da for money. *What would have happened to him if we hadn't taken him back to Islands?* I mused. I looked around the cottage. It was all very bare. There was an alcove in the bedroom and I noticed Granma's clothes hanging there. I decided to get rid of these before leaving. Then I made the decision to clear out the cottage completely, leaving no trace of who had lived there. I had plenty of time to spare. It didn't take me long to have everything piled up in the kitchen. I wondered if there was a 'tack' man who would take these items for me.

In the afternoon, I went out for a walk around Carrick. As I made my way into town, I was surprised at the number of shops. I went into a small shop which seemed to sell everything and had a good look around. I didn't have much money with me so I didn't buy anything. As I was leaving, I asked if there was a 'tack' man in town. The shopkeeper said, "Sure, yes, there is. His name is Matty Connell and he lives just over there in the corner cottage." I thanked him and made my way over to the cottage.

Matty Connell was a grand chap and said he would take everything and would be with me first thing in the morning. I was glad I'd done this and that I would be leaving the cottage empty.

Having arranged everything, I found my way to a pub and sat down with a beer. The publican said, "Would you be after having anything to eat, sir?" I realised I hadn't eaten for a long time and, feeling hungry, I asked him what they were serving. I was soon tucking in to a large lamb and potato pie. It was the best meal I'd had for days. After a pleasant few hours, I made my way back to the cottage and went straight to bed and slept soundly all night.

The following morning, I was up early. I decided to finish off the remaining oats and milk for my breakfast. I sat down and was soon tucking in. I looked around the kitchen as I ate. I realised the 'tack' man might be prepared to take small items of furniture, like the kitchen stools, the table and maybe other bits of furniture such as the bed and the bedding. I would let him have a look around and see if he was interested. I could see a way of making some money for Gramps. Sure enough, when he came, he took everything and the cottage was left empty. I had the grand sum of 75 pence to give to Gramps.

When he had gone, I knocked on the door of the next door neighbour. I told her Gramps had gone home with Da and wouldn't be returning. I asked for the name of the landlord so I could write to him. She offered to tell him Gramps had gone when next he called for the rent and I thanked her as this would save me writing a letter. We said our farewells and I told her we were grateful for all she had done for Gran and Gramps.

"Not at all!" she said. "It's been a pleasure. Sure, they've always been good neighbours and we'll be sorry now they've gone." She told me I would always be welcome whenever I visited Carrick. I thanked her and said goodbye.

I had a few hours to spare before my coach arrived so I walked down to the River Suir and sat on the bank watching the comings and goings of boats. There seemed to be regular sailings to Waterford. I saw two boats being laden with goods for market. I chatted to an old chap who was watching the world go by. He was glad to have someone to talk to. Like most old people he told me about the good old days. He remembered swimming in the river and the swimming races with his friends. He had known Gramps as a boy and remembered the good times they had together. He said all the boys had liked Granma. After a while, I made my way back to the cottage in readiness for my journey home.

¤

The Bianconi coach arrived in Carrick from Kilkenny and was soon ready to make its return journey. I hopped on board and was the only passenger. I chatted with the coach driver who told me he made this return journey six days a week. He said Ireland had changed since the introduction of the Bianconi coaches. He told me that his boss, Charles Bianconi, had come to Ireland from Italy in 1802. He'd started his coach business in 1815 and now had a network of coaching routes running from Belfast in the north and as far south as Cork in the south west.

"My boss, Charles Bianconi, is sometimes called 'King of the Road'! He now has nearly one thousand horses and over 50 coaches."

He continued, "He's now building a factory in Clonmel and he intends to build larger coaches which will hold up to twenty passengers and additional cargo. He's a man with great vision. He saw a need in the population for travel round the country and decided to cater for it."

I was amazed at this story. I wondered how an Italian immigrant had found the money to set up such a business. He must have a wonderful head for business. I was in awe of him. I realised if I had wanted to travel this far 30 years earlier, things would have been very different. In those days, you either walked or, if you were lucky enough, you went on horseback or in a private coach. Charles Bianconi was an example to us all.

When I arrived at Kells, I thanked the coach driver for a good journey and bade him goodbye. I looked around and could see no sign of Da waiting for me. I saw a pub and went in and treated myself to a porter.

I sat on a stool in a window alcove. Looking out of the pub window, I could see the coach stop and I waited there for Da to arrive. Eventually, I saw a donkey and cart approaching up the road with one person in it. As it drew nearer, I realised it was Uncle Thomas who had come to meet me, not Da. I was surprised to see him. He arrived at the coach stop and sat there waiting for me.

I finished my drink and hurried out to meet him. My first words were, "Hello, where is Da, is he alright?" He told me not to worry, everything was fine. Da was just tired after the journeys he'd made.

"I offered to come and fetch you to give him a rest." I hopped in the cart and we were soon wending our way home.

¤

We travelled as fast as we could but poor old Ned had done so many journeys recently, he was tired too. He was even slower than when he had pulled us to Carrick.

Our route home took us through Mullinahone. As we approached, it was nearing the end of the day and most farm work had stopped. Farm workers were making their way home and we passed them on the road. Many of them were itinerant workers with no place to live. They had built shacks on the side of the road. These shacks were not enough to shelter them when the weather was bad. It was all so different from us in our comfortable home and these scenes made me feel very uneasy.

Many vagrants were camped out along the way. These poor people were suffering. They had either been thrown out of their homes because of non-payment of rent or they had not been able to earn enough money to feed themselves and their families. This had been going on for many years and it was not surprising there was so much discontent in our land.

We had recently heard the government had decided to establish Poor Law Unions to help the poor and needy. Our local union was based in Callan. The Callan Poor Law Union covered a radius of ten miles. Both Islands and the small town of Mullinahone came within the Callan Union.

As we passed through Mullinahone, Thomas told me the Union had started work on building a workhouse in Callan which would house 600 people. I was glad to hear of this development and I hoped it would rid small towns like Mullinahone of the beggars who occupied the streets. Times were difficult for these unfortunate people but the workhouse would give them a roof over their heads and food in their stomachs. Of course, there would be a price to pay. A new tax called the Poor Law Rate would soon be introduced. This tax would cover the expenses of the Poor Law Union and the building of the new workhouse. We, amongst many others, were not happy at yet another tax which was suggested at 4p in the pound, but the money had to come from somewhere. Someone had to pay for these changes. We would have to wait and see how and when this tax would be introduced.

As we drove along, Thomas pointed out more beggars and vagrants camped alongside the road. He said that they were so poor that many of them took to robbing and thieving. Houses were sparsely furnished these days so they weren't able to steal much there, so they stole food in the markets and vegetables such as turnips from the fields. Some of them stole turf sods to warm their families in winter. Thomas said if they were caught stealing, they were sent to prison but this didn't deter them.

It was twilight when we arrived home at Islands. Mary came out to meet us. She was glad to see me back and said she'd missed me. She hadn't worried but it was the first time we'd been apart since we had married. I hopped off the cart and embraced her. It was good to be home after a difficult few days.

Gramps soon made himself at home with us. Mam had made up a bed for him in the parlour. This was ideal for him as he had difficulty climbing the stairs with his problem knees. His cottage in Carrick had been on one level so he wasn't used to stairs. Now, he was glad to be part of the family. He loved all the children and they quickly warmed to him. The poor, sad old man we had found in Carrick was no more. He was happy to be with us and was always grateful and smiling. It was wonderful to see what the change of scene had done for him.

That night, just before we all made our way to bed, I said to Gramps, "Goodnight. Oh, you'd better have this. Put it under your pillow for safe-keeping." I handed him the 75p from the tack man.

CHAPTER SIXTEEN

Life soon returned to normal. Tom Cahill had written and confirmed a place in the school for Dick so we now had to make final arrangements. Dick would be going to Thurles at the end of the summer and the term was due to start in September. He was so excited about going and he had packed everything he wanted to take with him well before the end of August.

It was a strange feeling when we set off for Thurles. Jack, Kate and Tom stood outside the house to wave us off. They were soon joined by Da, Mam, Gramps, Mary and Mikey. It was like history repeating itself. It took me back to the day when Da had taken me for my first term at Thurles.

Dick chatted all the way to Thurles. He was very enthusiastic and his excited mood brought back many memories for me. The journey was so familiar to me – I must have done it over a hundred times. The hedgerows were beginning to turn colour as we were now into autumn and there was a cold nip in the air.

I eventually left Dick at the school, saying, "Work hard and good luck. I'll come for you at half term." He waved me off on the front steps. It was strange to be going home without him, as though part of me had been taken away. I wondered if Da had the same feeling when he left me there all those years ago.

¤

When I arrived home, it was time for me to get my school ready in the barn. We were due to open in a week's time. I thought ahead to the winter and worried that we had no heating in the barn but there was nothing I could do to improve that. I remembered last year when the children had kept their outdoor clothes on all day and I hoped we would have a milder winter.

The number of pupils had doubled over the past few years and I had to provide extra facilities. We'd recently cut down an old tree so I asked Da if I could cut it up into logs. This would make excellent extra seating in the barn. He agreed and Uncle Thomas helped me with this. It was a big tree and we managed to get twelve good sized logs from it. Then, I set about making a new bench which would hold another six children.

During the holidays, Mary and I had made a trip to the slate quarries in Ahenny. My distant cousin Thomas Frisby was glad to see us. He had always given me a good deal on slates. We were given free rein in the quarry and we wandered round, looking at all the different types of slate. I invested in a number for the children to write on and I found a large one for myself which would be a useful teaching aid. I paid Thomas for these and we made our way back.

When we arrived home, Da said he would smooth the sharp edges off so the children wouldn't cut themselves. He did a grand job and they looked quite smart when he had finished. So, apart from heating, we were all set for the new term.

Gramps took a great interest in the school and often came down to visit us. He would sit and listen to the lessons, delighted to see how the children were improving. This was a new life for him. There had been little to interest him in recent years in Carrick. After a while, he asked me if he could read stories to the younger children. I was delighted with his offer and he became an important part of the school. He had, like Da, been educated in a hedge school in Carrick and was a firm believer in educating the young.

¤

In 1831, something happened which was going to alter the course of our lives. The government brought in a new law. They decided to set up national schools throughout the country, in towns and villages all over Ireland. I was concerned that this might mean I would have to close my school.

The government thought that hedge teachers had too much influence in the community. They wanted to stop this and said we needed to be brought into line. They believed that many of us didn't work to a set schedule. They didn't like this and wanted to standardise education throughout the country. I freely admit that I liked to spice up lessons to keep the children interested but I didn't think this was a bad idea. I wondered if teaching in these new schools would be like wearing a straitjacket?

I heard that in many parts of the north and west of the country the hedge teachers were a law unto themselves. Unfortunately, many of them were fond of their drink which gave all teachers a bad reputation in the eyes of the government. It was probably one of the many factors which made them act to get rid of us.

The government announced the new schools would work to a set curriculum and would be provided with suitable text books. Teachers would have to abide by new rules and regulations. District school inspectors would be appointed who would report to the newly established Department of Education. I hated the idea of my life being regulated by a higher authority. I thought it was fine in theory but I wondered how it would work in practice.

We realised it would take a long time for the new law to be implemented. It would be a mammoth job providing schools for every village and town in Ireland. We were so far out in the country that I was sure we would be last on the list. They would probably establish schools in the big towns first. The government didn't know how many children lived in rural areas like ours and they had a lot of investigations to carry out before deciding where to place the schools. Many would have to be built and then teachers found, so it would be a long time before the law touched us in our little rural backwater.

Mary agreed with me that we shouldn't worry about this threat.

Our little school wasn't going to disappear overnight. But I thought life might be very different in a few years' time. I wondered if I might eventually be employed at one of the new schools. If not, I would have to find another way to earn a living if my school closed down. Anyway, I wasn't too worried as I was sure there were plenty of other jobs I could turn my hand to.

¤

After our youngest son, Michael, was born in 1830 we had several scares with his health. He was slow to talk, slow to walk and suffered from numerous colds. The worst of all was the terrible croup. He would wake in the early hours of the morning, about two or three o'clock, coughing and struggling to get his breath. In a bad attack, he would go blue in the face; it frightened the life out of us. Mary would get up and wrap him in a warm blanket, take him downstairs and sit nursing him by the fire. During these months, Mary suffered from lack of sleep as well as worry so it was a harrowing time. We didn't know what to do for him. He was worse in winter even though we kept him indoors so he didn't get the cold winter air on his chest. On one occasion, we called in the handywoman to see if there was anything she could do to help. She made a few suggestions but none of them seemed to make any difference. I wasn't a believer in herbal remedies but we tried everything Joan suggested. As Mikey grew older, the occurrence of his ailment lessened. We wanted a better future for him but he was a delicate little thing and we hoped that healthier times were in store for him.

The other children were doing well. Kate was a great help to Mam in the house. She spent many hours stitching and sewing. Jack was now in full charge of the farm and it was doing well. Dick was in his element at school in Thurles. He liked it so much there that I don't think he wanted to come home in the holidays.

In the holidays, Dick always had his nose in a book. Whenever he could, he helped the priest at Ballingarry with Mass. His interest in religion was greater than ever since he had been at Thurles. He told me they sometimes had more than an hour's religious instruction each day and Saturdays were no exception. He'd been helping the monks during Sunday Mass. I was more than ever convinced in my mind he would want to be a priest when he left school.

Thomas was still at my school and was just a mediocre student. But he was keen to learn and, as he grew older, he took an interest in helping me. I suggested to him when he was 16 that he could become a monitor in the school.

The threat of a new school being set up in the vicinity by the government still lurked on the horizon but I was sure it would be several years away and I put it to the back of my mind.

While little Mikey was taking up so much of Mary's time, she was unable to help in the school. So now I was glad of Gramps' help.

¤

In 1834, riots broke out in Callan town, which was just over the border in County Kilkenny and just ten miles east of us. This was caused by the unhappiness which many people felt. They were not satisfied with their lot in life and thought they had been let down. The riots were broken up by the police who fired on the crowd. We would have to be more vigilant in future. This was too close to home!

We were now paying the Poor Law tax and we hoped it would be well spent. The Callan workhouse was eventually completed but within a few years it became severely overcrowded which led to its residents living in appalling conditions. Many of the poor souls were ill and some of them were unwell before they even arrived there. Disease spread quickly, with typhus and cholera being the most rampant and dangerous. There were many deaths, sometimes with whole families dying.

It was not surprising there was so much discontent in the country. Many people were suffering because they had no homes and they had been forced to go into the workhouse. They could see no improvement in their future lives.

That year ended sadly as Gramps passed away. He just died in his sleep one night. We were glad that the last few years of his life had been happy ones. The children all missed him as we all did. The end of a generation!

CHAPTER SEVENTEEN

Life proceeded very smoothly for the next few years, and little Mikey gradually improved in health. Mary was a wonderful mother and had nursed him until he started to show signs of improvement. She encouraged him to crawl and then to walk. I was full of admiration for the painstaking way she looked after him. But poor little Mikey would be worried with health problems all his life.

In the spring of 1835, my cousin David Frisby from Ballyduggan called on us to tell us he was getting married again. We weren't surprised. He had been struggling to look after his four young children since he lost his first wife in childbirth. He was marrying Catherine Tyrell, the daughter of one of his neighbours. For a year or two she had been helping him in the house and spent many hours looking after his children while he was out on the farm. She was a few years younger than David but she was a motherly soul and David was fond of her. His children loved her too and now she was going to take them on as her own children. David told us it had been a struggle since his wife had died but he was hoping for an easier life in future. We all looked forward to the wedding.

It was a bright sunny day when we all set off for the wedding. Mary and I travelled in our cart pulled by our old donkey. Jack and Catherine borrowed a cart from a neighbour and the other children walked, setting out an hour before us. The wedding ceremony was in Mullinahone in the ruins of the old church, though work had just started on a new building.

We made a great tribe and were soon joined by Kate and Brendan who turned up in Brendan's father's cart. I was familiar with this old church as we had worshipped there when we were children. We hadn't visited it for years as we had transferred to Ballingarry for Mass.

We met many distant relatives at David's wedding, some of them we had never even heard of. David's extended family of Frisbys from Killamery all turned up in force and Thomas Frisby and his wife came from Ahenny.

I didn't know how all these Frisbys fitted together in the larger Frisby clan but we were all accepted as part of the family. We knew we were related to them from far back, but no one knew exactly how.

A late arrival was James Frisby who had ridden up from Red Acres, near Mullinavat in southern Kilkenny. I was introduced to him and he tried to tell me how we were related. He seemed to know a lot about the wider family. He and his wife Eleanor had many children. The older ones were now grown up but the youngest was only three years old. Eleanor had stayed at home to look after the youngster. It was all very complicated. James told me he had other Frisby relations living near to him in Smithstown and it seemed that they all had large families, too. It was hard to remember all he told me.

When Mary asked me later how we were connected to James, I wasn't able to tell her as I had completely lost the thread. It was a long, convoluted story, covering many branches of the family who had dispersed to many places in the counties of Kilkenny, Tipperary and Waterford. Nevertheless, it was wonderful to see so many Frisbys at the gathering.

One evening, a few days after David's wedding, all the family were sitting round the kitchen table, talking about the wedding. The children wanted to know how we were related to the other Frisbys. They had played with their distant cousins at the wedding and wanted to know more about them. I told them we didn't know exactly how we were related but I explained that the link went far back before our time and even before Gramps' time.

I decided to tell them the story of one Francis Frisby who was thought to have been the first Frisby in Ireland. The story went back to the time of Oliver Cromwell who had caused so much trouble in our country. Cromwell had arrived with his army from England. His aim was to rid the nation of Catholicism and, as he travelled through the country, he destroyed many churches. I told them about his attack on Kilkenny Castle. When Cromwell's army arrived at the castle, the Duke of Ormond was not at home. They were met by his butler, Francis Frisby, who refused to surrender his master's silver plate. The soldiers were angry that Francis would not give in to them and they tortured him with lighted torches and he died of his wounds.

Francis Frisby had originally come from England and was a Protestant. The family were amazed to hear this and wanted to know more. They were horrified to hear they were descended from an English Protestant! We were all so 'Irish' and such good Catholics they could hardly believe the story. I explained to them that these first Frisbys in Ireland had married Irish girls and taken on their religion. There was a saying in Ireland that the English who married Irish girls became 'more Irish than the Irish'. So, our family had been Catholic since the mid-17th century, nearly two hundred years ago. We didn't know which part of England the Frisbys came from but it was probably in the east of the country, somewhere like Leicestershire, where the surname is most prevalent.

Dick was the first to comment.

"I'm surprised to hear we're descended from a Protestant. Two hundred years is not a long time. I can't understand why we don't know more about our ancestors." I said that 200 years equated to about eight generations and a lot of history could be lost in those years. I told him one of the only ways to trace a family was by searching in the parish records but during the years of the Penal Laws, these were non-existent. I also mentioned that there was another Frisby living in Ireland at the same time as Francis, called William Frisby. It was said, in the records, that he had supplied oxen to the military. This was interesting because the name William had come down in the Killamery Frisby line. I'd given them a lot to think about and I was sure there would be more questions in future.

Finally, I said, "You'll all be glad to know the soldier in charge of the attack on Kilkenny Castle and responsible for the murder of Francis Frisby, a man named Colonel Axtel, was eventually tried in London for murder and was hanged." It seemed to be a fitting end to a man who had caused so much trouble in Ireland.

We talked about David's wedding for several weeks and months, and we intended to stay in touch with our extended family. But life was busy and it was hard in those days to keep up a correspondence with far-flung relatives. It was easier to keep in touch with David as we lived closer to him than the other families. We weren't in contact with the Killamery Frisbys but we could find them if we needed to. They worshipped in Mullinahone, so they would be easy to locate.

Dick seemed to be the one member of the family with an interest in our history. One day, he said to me, "Pa, you said the Frisbys came to Ireland from England. Do you know the origin of our name?"

I wasn't surprised when he asked me this as Frisby was an uncommon name in Ireland. Fortunately, I had an answer for him. I told him there were a lot of places in the east of England with the suffix 'by', such as Derby, Grimsby, Whitby, Oadby, and many others. I explained that this suffix was of Scandinavian origin and meant 'farm' or 'homestead'. This was a hangover from the days when the Vikings invaded England and created their own territory in the east, known as Daneland. Frisby was the home of the 'Fris', possibly natives of the Frisian Islands.

I told him there was a village in Leicestershire called Frisby-on-the-Wreake, and the site of a deserted medieval village nearby, called Frisby, where only one or two houses remained. The Vikings had settled in many places in England, Scotland and Ireland when they invaded in about 900AD. Dick was thrilled to hear we might be descended from them and I knew he would try and discover more about the Vikings when he returned to school.

¤

It was not long before my cousin David wrote to tell us he and Catherine were expecting a baby to add to his family. It would be Catherine's first child but David's fifth but it would not be their last. Catherine was delighted at the thought of having a child of her own alongside David's four children from his first marriage.

¤

In 1837, the Presentation Brothers set up a school on Glen Road in Ballingarry. I was intrigued and decided to pay them a visit on my next free day. When I did, I found a very impressive set-up. They had over 50 boys and girls on their books and there was a waiting list of 50 more. They didn't have enough staff to take on any more children.

On my way home, I thought back to the days when I was teaching in Thurles. Something struck me - Dick was now 17-years-old and soon he would leave school and start looking for his first job. Teaching in Ballingarry would be ideal for him. He would come with a reference from the Brothers in Thurles and I thought he might like to be involved in this new school. I mentioned this to Mary when I arrived home and she agreed it would be ideal for him. She had been wondering what he would do when he left school.

The end of the summer term came and I went to Thurles to collect Dick. When I arrived, I had a quick chat with him. I could tell he was sad to be leaving school. He went off to pick up his belongings and, when he disappeared, I had a word with Tom Cahill. I told him about the Brothers' school in Ballingarry but he already knew about it. I asked him if he thought Dick would make a good teacher.

He realised immediately what I was thinking. He replied "I know the Brothers in Ballingarry are looking for a teacher. Yes, Richard would be a great help to them. He would do well there. I have no problem recommending him if it's what he wants."

I couldn't believe our luck. It was so unusual for a young Catholic boy to go straight into employment. I warned Tom, "I haven't told Dick yet about the school and he may have other ideas. So please don't mention this to him. I'll tell him about it on our way home. Thank you for everything. I'll let you know what happens."

Dick appeared in the doorway and shook hands with Tom, saying goodbye and thanking him for all he had done. We made our way to our cart. I knew Dick wouldn't want me to push him into a job. If he wanted it, the idea must come from him. On the way home, I told him all the family news. He was glad to hear young Mikey was improving and said he had prayed for him every day. I told him about the Brothers' school in Ballingarry. He appeared interested and when I told him about the waiting list, he said, "Where will they get more teachers?"

"I expect they'll find someone locally," I replied, off-handedly.

Dick was quiet for the rest of the way home. Just before we arrived, he said, "Pa, do you think I would make a good teacher?" I said I thought he was quite young but I had taught in Thurles at his age. I said he should go and visit the school if he was interested. We left it at that.

From there, things progressed rapidly. Dick went straight to Ballingarry the next day and introduced himself. He came home with a big smile on his face.

"They've offered me a job, on trial at first. I can start next term, provided Mr. Cahill gives me a good reference."

This was a time for rejoicing! Two sons would now be gainfully employed. It was justification, indeed, for me opening my school and teaching my own children. Mary and I decided we would have a small party to celebrate.

¤

We noticed during the summer that Jack was friendly with a young local girl called Catherine Ryan. The Ryans lived in Modeshill, a few miles away. The couple had met at church and Jack was seeing her occasionally in the evenings when he wasn't busy on the farm. He complained he didn't have enough time to see her. Imagine our surprise when, one day, they both arrived at Islands saying, "We've got some good news for you." Jack had asked Catherine to marry him. They were going to talk to the priest the next day. We were delighted for the couple but one thought ran through my mind, *Where are we all going to sleep?*

I needn't have worried about that. Jack took me on one side and told me Catherine's parents had offered them a room when they were married. This solved one problem but I wondered if it would lead to another. I asked him if he would continue to work on our farm but he said he had no problem continuing that. I wondered if this was achievable – I had heard stories of young men going to live with their in-laws who became so involved with their new family, they never looked back on their real family. I asked Jack how big Ryan's farm was. It was slightly bigger than ours. I asked who worked it.

"Catherine has two brothers who help their father. I'm not going to let you down, Pa. The Ryans won't be asking me to work for them. We're just going to live there."

I was relieved to hear this.

¤

It was now time for Tom to leave school. He would be able to help on the farm. Although he had tried to help me as a monitor in school for a few weeks, it hadn't worked out. He didn't enjoy it and I knew he would prefer working in the fresh air. To a certain extent I was hedging my bets – for if Jack did spend less and less time with us, at least Tom would be able to carry on some of his work.

Jack and Catherine were married in August. The ceremony was performed by the priest in Mullinahone. After the wedding, we had a party at Islands. It was a very happy affair. The Ryan family joined us and we had a house full of friends and relatives. It was the first time we had had such a big gathering for a while. There was much merriment and Da showed his skill on the violin while Uncle Thomas played the pipes. We danced, we sang, we ate and we drank. We were all very happy.

Jack and Catherine eventually made their way to Modeshill and we all waved them off.

"Good luck!" was the cry heard ringing out as they disappeared into the darkness.

Kate had invited her boyfriend Brendan Molloy to the celebrations. It was good to see she had a special friend. Their friendship seemed to be serious and I wondered if we had another wedding in the offing.

¤

I often thought about the future and realised that, when the new national schools were set up, it might not be possible for me to teach any more. I didn't know if I would be accepted by the Education Board. So, I started thinking about what I could do to earn some money. As so many older people couldn't read or write, it had occurred to me they might like someone to write letters for them from time to time. I could become a scribe and I could also write wills and help people with their tenancy agreements. I decided I would start to do this in my spare time. Hopefully, people in our locality would get to know I offered this service. In the next school holiday, I set about telling people at church what I was able to do to help them. Bit by bit, work came my way. It was slow at first but soon picked up. Mary said if it continued to go well, I would have to give up teaching. I didn't want to do that so I kept both jobs going. I had plenty of time in the evenings, at weekends and in the school holidays to do my scribe work. Soon people were knocking on the door most evenings asking for my help as word got round the neighbourhood. To avoid the family hearing everyone's business, I took my customers into the parlour to talk to them about their needs. It was good that Gramps was no longer sleeping in there as it would have made things difficult. During his later years, he had taken to going to bed quite early every evening and the room would not have been available to me.

¤

Mikey's health had improved a lot so Mary wasn't spending all her time looking after him now. She started helping me in school again and I was glad of this, particularly as we were missing Granpa's visits. The children missed his story telling but Mary took his place and Mikey joined us in the infants' section. He was glad to have his mother there.

Kate was seeing more of Brendan and one day they came home together from Mass. They came into the kitchen and Brendan asked if he could have a word with me.

"Yes, of course," I said, and he indicated we should step outside. He didn't want the rest of the family to hear our conversation. He shut the door behind us and coughed nervously before saying, "Mr Frisby, Kate and I have been seeing each other now for nearly two years. We want to be married. Will you give us permission?" I was amazed at the formality of his request. I replied that nothing would please me more. I asked him when they intended to tie the knot.

"Kate doesn't want to wait around for too long so it will be as soon as possible."

I was glad Kate was to marry such a pleasant young boy and I had no hesitation in giving them my permission.

"We must tell the family the good news," I said. We went into the house and the family all gathered around in the kitchen to hear what we had to say. Everyone was pleased as they all liked Brendan. Kate was blushing and I asked them where they would live. Brendan said his parents had offered them a room at their home. We would be sorry to lose Kate but I knew she was marrying into a good family and we were happy for her. Brendan was apprenticed as a shoemaker to his father so it would suit him to live over the shop.

"Well," I said, "this calls for a celebration!" We all had a mug of cider and wished them luck in the future.

Mam was going to miss Kate as she'd been such a help around the house but she'd known this would come one day and she was pleased for her.

Kate and Brendan were married in the spring, after Lent, and they were lucky with the weather. We had the wedding breakfast at our house and we partied into the night. Brendan's parents and relatives arrived in a large cart drawn by a horse and the newly married couple would go home with them after the party.

Now that Kate and Brendan had moved out, there were only seven of us left in the house. Mam, Da, Mary, me, Dick, Thomas and young Mikey. We were able to spread ourselves out a bit. Mary and I slept in the room over the parlour with Mam and Da. There was a curtain in the room which divided the room in two which gave us a certain amount of privacy. The boys slept in the room over the kitchen.

¤

Two years later, Jack was still happily settled living in Modeshill with Catherine. Times had been sad for her as she had lost both her parents. After their passing, Jack took over the tenancy of Ryan's farm. Again, I worried that he would spend time working on the Ryan's farm and would neglect us. *Is this the beginning of the end of our farm?* I thought. I need not have been concerned for Kate's two brothers still ran the Ryan farm and they said there was not enough work there for Jack.

¤

Our landlord was an Englishman called Richard Cormick. We rarely saw him as he lived most of the year in England. When he was in Ireland, he stayed just down the road at Mohober House. He was one of the Irish 'absentee landlords' who trusted his agent to look after his lands and properties when he was away. Mohober House was quite large and much bigger than any other house in the district, and like most large houses, it had many acres of land.

In 1837, there was a disturbance outside Mr. Cormick's house. Jack went out to see what was happening. He came running back and told us a posse of police together with the district sheriff were outside the house, accompanied by soldiers from the 24th light foot brigade who had come to collect tithes and rent arrears. They couldn't find Mr. Cormick and were unable to complete their mission and left empty handed. This was a strange event and to our knowledge the police never returned.

Not long after that we heard that a relative of Mr. Cormick, who lived at Coolaghmore House, near Callan just over the border in County Kilkenny, had also attempted to defer payment of taxes. Rumour had it that 50 police and a detachment from the Royal Artillery had turned up at his house. It was good to know these landlords were being held to account. We always paid our rent on time, so we didn't think they should get away with defaulting.

¤

So, the years passed. Dick was happy teaching at Ballingarry. Tom was helping Jack on the farm; and young Mikey was progressing slowly at school. In a few years, Mikey would leave school and we thought that he, too, would help on the farm. He wasn't as strong as his brothers but we thought physical work might help to mature his young body. He was a happy lad in spite of all his health problems. We saw Kate and Brendan at Mass every week. They were both happy and often came back with us for a meal after church.

Not long after Kate's wedding, she and Brendan proudly told us they were expecting their first child. We were delighted. It was to be the first of many. Kate and Brendan would make wonderful parents.

In 1838, Jack and Catherine had their first child, a son, whom they named Richard. He was our first grandson and we were very proud. Then, in 1842 they had a daughter whom they called Catherine. We didn't feel old enough to be grandparents!

CHAPTER EIGHTEEN

The night of the 6th January 1839 was one never to be forgotten by many people living in the west of Ireland. It would forever be remembered as the 'Night of the Big Wind', a huge storm that had arisen off the west coast. The Feast of the Epiphany falls on January 6th and many believed the end of the world was nigh. There was no storm warning and gusts of winds reached epic speeds. It lasted many hours throughout the dark night, causing hundreds of deaths as well as damaging and wiping out houses all over the country. It was stormy at sea, with hundreds of shipwrecks. Gigantic waves were coming in from the Atlantic and in County Clare they were high enough to break over the Cliffs of Moher, which are the highest cliffs in the country.

Several miles inland, fish were found on branches of trees having come in on waves from the sea. It was the worst storm to hit our country for over 300 years. It was a devastating and frightening experience that lived long in our memories. We didn't suffer the worst of the gales as we lived in the east of the country. Certainly, we experienced bad weather but nothing like the strong winds experienced by people in the west of the country.

¤

In 1844, we lost Da. Two years before he had cut back his coopering work and started to work only half days. But even this took its toll on him and he said to me one day, "I've had a good life. It's time I stopped working and let my poor old body rest. My aches and pains are now the worst they've ever been." I was sorry for him.

He stopped work altogether. He had given all his life to providing for his family and never wanted to stop. He was worried about how we would manage in future.

"Da, you mustn't worry. Jack has built up the farm and it provides for all our needs. Dick is now making a small contribution to the family budget and I give a small amount from the school fees. Also, there is the money we get from the baskets. The ladies are still making them and there is no reason why that should stop."

Da died just a week after he had stopped working. It was a great shock to us all. He had been around forever. He was 82 years old and had lived at Islands for 55 years. We couldn't imagine life without him. We are never prepared for these events in life. When it's your father, it's difficult to believe it's happened. Da had been sitting in the garden in the sunshine and fell asleep. It was a warm summer's day and so we left him there. Tea time came and he didn't appear. We wondered when he was going to come in.

"I'll go and look for him," Mikey said. He soon came running back, saying, "Pa, Ma, come quickly. Gramps is not answering me."

We all ran out and it was a sorry sight to see. My dear old father was sitting in the evening sunshine with his eyes closed. He would never open those eyes again but he looked happy and I think he was. He had gone to sleep in the sunshine and he never woke up again. He had supported his family all his life and now there was nothing more he could do.

There was a huge funeral for Da. We were surprised at the number of farmers and neighbours who arrived at the wake. Many of the farmers had been his customers and our neighbours had known him for many years. My lasting memory of Da is of him sitting in his chair in the garden with his eyes closed and the hint of a smile on his face. Life had to go on without him. We grieved for him in the knowledge he had been the mainstay of our existence at Islands, but most of all we had loved him and would miss him terribly.

¤

Now, everyone looked to me as head of the family. Jack was older than me and if he had stayed living at Islands, this burden would have fallen on him. But now I felt responsible for them all. This weighed heavily on me and it was only with Mary's help that I was able to shoulder it. It shouldn't have been a problem but it was like a millstone round my neck. I realised I was responsible for so many people. I wondered what the future would hold and how I would cope. I also wondered if Jack would ever move back to Islands and take up his position as head of the house. If he did, I would welcome him gladly as it would take the pressure off me.

¤

A few weeks went by and we had good news and bad. The good news was that Kate gave birth to her son. The bad news was that we lost Mam. She was working in the kitchen and was suddenly struck with a pain in her stomach. She sat down for a few minutes and tried to gather herself but the pain only worsened. When we arrived home from school, we found her sitting in the kitchen, her face deathly white. We were very worried.

We helped her upstairs to bed and sent for the handywoman. Joan arrived quickly and administered her herbal remedies. These had the effect of settling Mam down and she fell asleep for the night. Joan said she would call again in the morning but Mam was no better the next day and Joan told us to call for a doctor as there was nothing more she could do. She said Mam needed a medically qualified doctor. Dick rode off to Ballingarry to call on him but we didn't know when he would come. Meanwhile, Mam was given another dose of the herbal remedy which quietened her down again and she fell asleep.

I went to check on her at midday and to my horror I found she wasn't breathing. She had slipped away without any of us with her to say goodbye. At least her passing was peaceful. When the doctor arrived, he confirmed her death and provided us with a death certificate. It was a shock to lose both our parents in such a short time.

It had happened so quickly and we were all stunned. Coming so soon after Da's death, it was even more difficult to take in. Mary said she thought Ma didn't want to go on living without Da. All was quiet in the house. I rode to Mullinahone and arranged for the undertaker to call. Thankfully, he took care of everything for us and we had little to do. He arranged the funeral service and put a notice in the newspaper.

The neighbours came to offer their condolences. Mam was laid out on her bed and someone put her rosary in her hand and lit two candles, one on each side of the bed. She was dressed in her Sunday best. The day before the funeral, someone sat with her all day. The neighbours came in to help and worked in shifts. They all prayed at her bedside with their rosaries. On the day of the funeral, the banshees arrived but I hated this ancient practice. Old women dressed in black visiting the houses of the dead, sitting near the body and making a monotonous wailing noise. They said they were praying for the soul of the departed. That horrible noise stayed with me for many days. It reminded me of Granma's funeral in Carrick all those years ago. We remembered the neighbours there saying the banshees would curse us for sending them away. We had laughed at that but, thankfully, the threatened curse never happened.

I made sure all the children were scrubbed clean for the funeral. A carriage came for Mam's coffin and there was a hush in the house while it was carried out. When it was placed outside on two chairs, the banshees started their lament again. They made a monotonous wailing sound – a lamentation for the dead, partly poetic. They chanted, "You were a good wife and mother", and "You were kind to your neighbours", and "You will be sorely missed", over and over again. This keening continued until the undertakers put the coffin on to the carriage.

Fortunately, the banshees didn't follow us to church and I was glad to see them go on their way. I told Mary how Da had sent them away from Granma's funeral.

That was the last we saw of Mam. We followed the coffin to Ballingarry for the funeral. Many neighbours and friends turned up for the service. I was pleased to see Mam had been so well liked. We buried her in the old graveyard at Modeshill, where we had laid Da to rest. They were together again.

The wake followed and, as usual, there was singing and dancing and everyone said what a wonderful woman Mam had been. I was glad to hear these words but they would not bring her back to us. I didn't like funerals or wakes but we had to do them.

¤

Both my parents had now gone which made me sad. But, as one generation went so another arrived – with the birth of Jack and Kate's children, another generation of the family.

Mary and I were finding it tough since the deaths of Mam and Da. The well-being of the family was in our hands and I didn't know how we were going to shoulder the burden. I didn't think Jack would ever return to take his position as the eldest son so the family always looked to me for advice.

After Mam's funeral, Mary and I sat down and took stock of our position. We should have done it earlier but we had taken a few weeks to get over Da's death. The death of Mam, following on so closely after Da, focused our minds. Mary took over all of Mam's household duties. I hadn't been trained in coopering so I couldn't take over that and I wondered if I should have arranged for one of our son's to be apprenticed to Da. Anyway, it was too late now. An apprenticeship lasts several years and I should have thought of that many years ago. I wondered how I could have been so negligent. If one of our boys had shown an interest in the business, everything would have been so different. Life would be much easier if we could keep the business running.

The family's main source of income had always come from the coopering and basket making. Now it had changed. Our main income would now come from the farm so it looked as if we would have to re-double our efforts there. The problem was that the farm income was cyclical so I decided to talk to Jack as he had been in sole charge for several years so he would have some ideas about increasing its productivity.

A few days later, Jack and I discussed the farm and its future. Jack had already made many improvements over the years. He was confident there was still more he could do. He said there were two fields which had lain fallow for several years and he would plant these with different crops. He suggested barley for the lower field but he was still undecided about the upper field. He had a few ideas and wanted to research them before making a decision. He said he wasn't able to predict the outcome of crops we hadn't grown before but wheat and oats would continue to be our main crops. He stressed on me that we should never forget that bad weather could affect everything.

Jack had great ideas of rearing cattle. At that moment, we had only two cows but he wanted to increase the numbers. There was a farmer in Modeshill, next to the Ryans, who had a bull which he loaned out to farmers. If we borrowed the bull, we could rear young calves. The alternative was to take a short cut and buy calves from market. In any event, he was keen to increase the size of our herd.

We had a small flock of sheep and he'd already arranged for the shearer to come in a few weeks' time, and the wool would be sold at market.

It seemed Jack had thought of everything but there was one thing worrying me.

"How much did Da pay you, Jack?" I asked him. He told me the amount varied depending on how much Da could afford to pay him. "I've always managed," he said. I was concerned as I couldn't see where the money was coming from to pay him in the next few months. He knew things were going to be difficult for a while but I told him that hopefully, when things improved, there would be an increase in his wage.

"With hard work, I'm sure we'll get by," he said.

Before Jack left, I asked him how much help he had from Uncle Thomas, and his brothers, Tom and Mikey. He said Uncle Thomas had spent most of his time in the workshop with Da and had helped him on only a very few occasions. Tom had been helping him for some time. Every morning, he cleaned out the cowhouse and put down hay for the animals and later helped Jack in the fields with the crops, the cows or the sheep. Jack said he would not be able to cope without Tom who took a lot of weight off his shoulders.

Mikey's only involvement was in the dairy where he milked the cows. At that moment, with only two cows, there wasn't enough milk to make butter.

"When we eventually have more cows," Jack said, "we will have more milk and Mikey will be able to make butter and even, one day, perhaps cheese." Jack said he thought there were many more things Mikey could do to help.

When Jack had gone, Mary and I realised we had to find money to pay people and we didn't know where it would come from. We had a quick look around the workshop to see if Da kept business accounts and couldn't find any. Unfortunately, we had to cancel some outstanding orders. I didn't like letting Da's customers down but there was no alternative. I wished I had discussed the business with Da. If I had, I wouldn't be floundering now.

That evening I said to Mary I was surprised that Da had not made any arrangements in the event of his death. I also wondered why he had been so secretive about how much money the business was worth. It wasn't like him to leave things undone. We still wondered where the money had been spent. We realised he hadn't expected to go so quickly.

Mary asked me about the school. She wondered if I would continue to run it. I told her I hadn't thought of stopping because, although the rewards were small, they were better than nothing. I reminded her that my scribe writing brought in a small income too.

The lack of money was concerning me. I couldn't see how we

were going to manage. I had a restless night and all sorts of terrible thoughts went through my mind as I lay awake. I thought, *What if we can't pay the rent? What if we use up all our food stores?* I envisaged us as waifs, walking the country roads, looking for work, begging for food and for a roof over our heads. Things seemed so much worse at night as I turned these things over and over in my mind. I had never been so concerned for my family's future in all my life.

Mary knew I wasn't sleeping well. In the morning, she suggested we should go to the workshop and have a good look round.

"We might have missed something," she said.

We got to the workshop early. Uncle Thomas was there and didn't seem to be doing much work. Soon we would have to tell him that we were going to close the business. I wasn't looking forward to this. It was going to be difficult. I asked him what he was doing and he said he was preparing one or two orders that were ready to go out. We let him continue and started to look round to see if we had missed anything the day before.

At one end of the workshop there was a small area which Da had used as an office. Here, he recorded all the orders in a ledger. I was surprised at how comprehensive it was. It contained the names and addresses of customers, the full details of their orders with measurements, and finally the cost he charged. I was surprised at the prices he had been charging. They were far higher than I had envisaged. I showed the ledger to Mary.

"I wonder what happened to all this money?" she said.

The business was far more profitable than we had ever imagined.

"We must look into this," I said.

I had a word with Uncle Thomas and asked him how much Da had been paying him. We were surprised at Da's generosity and realised Uncle Thomas had been a great help to Da. I still didn't tell him yet that we were closing the business as I wanted to get a better idea of what was involved.

I had another search in Da's little office. I looked into his filing drawers which contained old paperwork such as old invoices and copies of orders. Underneath all this, at the back of the bottom drawer, I found a large cardboard box. I lifted it out and put it on the desk. I opened it and took out the papers I found inside. I was astounded at what I found.

"Look at this, Mary!" I said.

She came across and looked at what I was holding.

"It's a will," I said. "The last will and testament of John Frisby of Islands."

We were both staggered and couldn't wait to read it.

It made for very interesting reading. Da had gone to a lot of trouble to ensure all was left in 'apple pie' order. If we had found the will earlier, it would have saved us all our worry. I was amazed at what I read. Da was leaving all his worldly goods to me, which was a surprise, presumably because I was the oldest son still living at home. He said the lease on the house and land should be assigned to his wife, Mary, but in the event of her demise it should pass to Jack, provided he continued to run the farm. Da wanted the barn and surrounding land assigned to me for the purpose of running my school. A clause in the will allowed Mary and me to live in the house for the rest of our lives. It was an astonishing document and Da had obviously given a lot of thought to the future. I was glad he thought so much of Jack as he had made a good job of looking after the farm and deserved this reward.

I realised now that, as Mam had died, the lease of the house and land would pass straight to Jack.

Mary took another piece of paper out of the box and began studying it. She passed it to me.

"Dick, you should take a look at this. I can't understand it."

It was a list of monies Da had accumulated over the years. We knew nothing about this and I wondered where the money was. At the bottom of the page, it said, "Held in the account of John Frisby at the bank in Callan, County Kilkenny." I was astonished. It amounted to several hundred pounds. If it was correct, all our worries were over.

We sat down and tried to take this news in. It was clear now why Da had made occasional trips to Callan. He had been going to the bank. I wondered if Mam had known about this. The business was far more profitable than any of us had realised. It was no wonder Da continued working until the day he died. He was building up a pot of money to leave to us. One thing was clear, he never spent money on himself. His family meant everything to him and he wanted us to benefit from his hard work.

Mary and I went back to the house and decided to tell Jack about Da's will. Mary asked me if I minded that the house was passing to Jack but I told her I thought it was the fairest way. After all, even though Jack was not living at Islands, he was the eldest son and it was his right to inherit. Also, he had been running the farm for years now and, without him, the land would have lain fallow. Da would never have managed without Jack's help on the farm.

It looked as if our worries were over. I would be able to sleep tonight, knowing that we would have a roof over our heads and we were not going to be thrown out!

Da had never charged me any rent for the barn and had been generous in leaving a part of the lease to me. This meant I could continue to run the school rent free. We thought Da's will was fair to all. Mary said she was glad he had left the lease to Jack but had not forgotten us.

"We can continue to live here and we will still have the school," I said. "I am content. Jack has worked hard and deserves to take over the house and the land." We both agreed.

We wondered if Jack would now bring Catherine and their children to live with us. I knew they were firmly established at Modeshill but now that Jack had inherited the lease on Islands, they might change their minds and come to live with us.

Before we saw Jack again, we made a visit to the bank in Callan.

We had a meeting with the manager and showed him Da's will and death certificate. The bank account was transferred into my name and I immediately felt much easier about our future. I would be able to pay Jack and Uncle Thomas their wages and I had time to sort everything out.

Like us, Jack was amazed at the contents of the will. He had never expected the house and land to fall to him as he had moved away to Modeshill. It took him a while to get used to the news. I asked him if he would be moving back to Islands with Catherine and the children. He said he would talk to Catherine. They had never expected this – it was like a bolt from the blue.

CHAPTER NINETEEN

We all breathed a sigh of relief now that we knew we were financially secure. We couldn't see any problems in the foreseeable future. We relaxed a little and it didn't seem to be so urgent to tie everything up. I decided to keep Uncle Thomas on for a little longer. He could help us tidy up the workshop. We would have to turn out all Da's tools and someone suggested I should sell these. I was glad to do anything which would bring in a little extra money.

After a week or two, I had a word with Uncle Thomas and told him we were closing the cooperage business down. He was not surprised.

"Aye, I gathered this when you cancelled the outstanding orders and started clearing out the workshop. Do you think you'll be able to give me full time work on the farm when all the business has been settled up?" I told him he would have to talk to Jack about that. I explained to him that Jack might be moving back to Islands and would have complete control over the farm. He was surprised and asked me if Mary and I would be staying in the house and he was glad to hear we would still be around.

That evening, Mary and I discussed the future of the school. Even though we wouldn't be paying rent for the barn or for our board, we wanted the school to stand on its own two feet but it was only just breaking even. We talked about how we could make it more profitable. We had two options: either increase the size of the school or increase the fees. Many parents had difficulty finding the money for the fees so I didn't want to increase them so decided to enrol more pupils.

I told Mary about a few ideas I'd been having. I thought the workshop, which was now empty, would be an ideal place for a school. It was slightly larger than the barn and it had heating which would be wonderful in the cold winter months. We wouldn't have to wear our overcoats indoors when it was freezing outside. Another advantage was that it was much lighter than the barn as it had proper windows.

"That's an excellent idea, provided Jack agrees," Mary said. We were hopeful he would agree to this, particularly when he realised he would be able to use the barn for farm storage.

Mary said we should continue the basket making side of the business. She was happy to run it for us. Several local ladies made baskets at home and they still came along in the mornings to pick up the raw materials. They took these home with them, returning the baskets when they were completed. It suited these ladies to work at home as they could fit the work in around their household duties. They were glad, too, of the few pennies they earned. I hadn't given much thought to this subsidiary side of the main business and I told Mary I was glad about her offer.

"It makes more sense if a lady runs it, as all the employees are women."

"Now that Mikey is at school all day, I'll definitely have time for it." She said she would love to do it.

Everything was beginning to slot into place nicely. I hoped Jack would let me have the workshop as a schoolroom as it would put the school on a much firmer footing and it was big enough to take additional pupils.

A few days later, Jack popped in to see us and told us he and Catherine had decided to move to Islands. They were looking forward to it. He wanted to know what the sleeping arrangements would be. I suggested that he and Catherine and their children could have the room over the kitchen which should suit them. It was the warmest room in the house in winter as it was directly over the kitchen fire and I thought this would be good for their young children. Mary and I, together with Tom, Dick and Mikey, would sleep in the room over the parlour. Jack seemed pleased with this arrangement and said, "Catherine is looking forward to the move."

I took the bull by the horns and told Jack about my idea for the schoolroom. He agreed it was a good plan and was pleased that he would be able to use the barn for storage. Now that the farm was expanding, it would be essential.

I told Jack that Mary had offered to look after the basket making. We were both pleased as he, like me, was sad Da's business was going but at least this small part could be saved. Mary needed space to store the reeds and some of the tools and he said she could store them in the barn.

I assured Jack that he and his family would be in charge of the house. Mary and I didn't want to get in their way. Jack said Catherine had been wondering how things would work out. It was obvious that Catherine liked to have the kitchen to herself and Mary was glad to hear this. Her time would be full with the basket making business and the help she gave me in school. She didn't mind Catherine taking over in the kitchen. It was clear we were boarders in the house but we were welcome and treated as part of the family. This was often the custom in Ireland, with several generations all living in one house.

We called all the family together the following weekend and told them about the changes. Firstly, I read Da's will. Everyone was surprised to hear the contents. I had many questions to answer and I was glad I'd discussed everything with Jack and Mary beforehand. I explained to them there was a clear division of duties: Jack was in total control of the farm, and Tom and Mikey would help him. The school would be moving into Da's old workshop and Mary would run the basket making business from the barn. I told them Jack, Catherine and the children would be moving in the following weekend and Catherine would be in charge of the kitchen. We were all glad Jack's family were coming to live with us. It would be good to hear the sound of young children about the place again.

The family were pleased with the new arrangements. Now things had been finalised, we all looked forward to working together to make a success in memory of Da.

Jack and I didn't go into any great detail about finance. At the first opportunity, I told him I would be in overall charge of this. However, he would have to set the wages of anyone he employed on the farm. He would also have to decide what to charge for our produce when it went to market. He knew it was important to make a profit but was glad to have only a minimal involvement in financial matters.

The next time I went to Callan, I went to see the bank manager again. I opened three new accounts, one for the farm, another for the school and the final one for the basket making. This was necessary so we could see how each part of our enterprise was performing. Sometimes I wondered if I would ever understand the ins and outs of it all.

¤

I was glad we were now into the summer holidays. Apart from helping with the harvest, I decided to put my efforts into the school in its new home. Uncle Thomas had made a good job of turning out the workshop and it now stood empty. We didn't fully realise the size of it until everything had been moved out – it was much larger than we had thought. It hadn't been cleaned properly or painted since it was first built so it now looked quite drab. This was our first job. With the help of my uncle, we set about cleaning the building and we were amazed at the difference it made. Mary asked if it was necessary to paint the walls.

"A lick of paint will make all the difference, you'll see!" I wanted it to be clean and fresh for the new term in the autumn. Soon, it looked as good as new. I was delighted.

Uncle Thomas showed me how the wood-burning stove worked. He said that if he ran out of wood, he had sometimes used turf from our turf pile. We looked forward to a nice warm schoolroom during the cold winter months. Our last job was to clean the windows. One window looked out on Slievenamon in the distance, while the other faced our fields at the back of the house. All we had to do now was to bring the school furniture up from the barn.

One day, Mary and I went to Kilkenny to buy supplies for the school. We arrived home with paper, ink, pencils, chalk and several new books. We bought a maths book, an English primer and an atlas.

Over the summer months when we had been out walking, I had collected goose quills from the countryside, alongside the King's River. I decided to instruct the children how to fashion these into pens. I was pleased with the progress we were making.

Uncle Thomas was still living next door with his family and I knew that I would soon have to tell him there was no full-time work for him in future. He came to talk to me one day and told me he had made up his mind to emigrate. I was surprised to hear his decision but at the same time relieved. My uncle had been a great help to me since Da had died but we both knew his days with us were numbered. I suggested that if he stayed, Jack might be able to give him part-time work such as helping at busy times like harvest. However, he was adamant.

"No. Me and the wife have talked about it for hours and we both agree it's best we go. We appreciate the time we've had here at Islands; it's been so much better than the life we had in Carrick. But we've heard tales of opportunity in America and we want to go now before we get any older." I thanked him for all he had done for us and said we would be sorry to lose them.

We had a big send-off party for my uncle which we held in our house; Thomas' little cottage was too small for a large crowd. It was another good party and enjoyed by all. We let our hair down, dancing and cavorting about and having a grand time. When the dancing stopped, we had a good sing-song and by the end of the evening we were all hoarse. I loved to see the family enjoying themselves like this. Times like this were too rare.

We were sad Thomas and his family were going and we looked back on some of the good times we had had with them. Having a relative as our next-door neighbour had brought us comfort. But there was one good thing – Thomas' son George decided to stay on in their little house and not emigrate with his family. George helped Jack from time to time and was quite happy to be employed on a part-time basis. He often found work on neighbouring farms and quite liked travelling about and working for other families. This suited them both and Jack only called on his help when it was really needed. We wondered why George had decided not to go with his family to America. We were soon to find out. He had become friendly with a young girl called Mary Marnell and he didn't want to go away without her. Eventually, they were married and lived very happily in the little one storey cottage next door to us.

¤

Jack and Catherine and their children had now been living with us for several weeks and the new arrangements were working out well. Jack's two children were Richard, who had been born in 1838, and Catherine, born in 1842, and these young children brought much joy to us. They played the same games as we had when we were young and they made friends with our neighbours' children. Laughter could be heard as they played hide 'n' seek – they found all the nooks and crannies we used to hide in years ago. Another favourite game was tig when they chased each other all over the place.

Once, young Catherine fell and rushed into the house with blood pouring from her knee. She cried out for her mother who soon pacified her and cleaned up her leg. Luckily, it was only a minor scratch and she was soon back outside with the others.

In 1844, Catherine became pregnant with her third child. With about two weeks to go, she was heavily pregnant so Mary took over some of the household duties to relieve her. The handywoman was anticipating a call from us at any time. She knew Catherine's time was near and came one day to make sure all was well. She expressed surprise at Catherine's condition. She was feeling very tired and her legs were badly swollen, and was finding it difficult to get around. The handywoman was a girl called Maureen who had taken over from her mother, Joan, who had retired a few years ago. Maureen ordered Catherine to stay in bed. It was difficult to keep pregnant women in bed, so she read the riot act to her, telling her if she didn't comply it might be the end of her and the end of the new baby.

We were all very frightened at this prospect so we all did what we could to help. Mary took over the household duties completely. Ten days later, another daughter was born to Jack and Catherine whom they named Bridget. Fortunately, mother and baby were both well and it was not long before Catherine was back in the kitchen again, looking after the family.

The young children loved their new baby sister and enjoyed pushing her about in an old baby cart which Uncle Thomas had made for his children from old pieces of wood he had found lying about.

CHAPTER TWENTY

Not long after the birth of Jack's new daughter, we were visited again by Sean the tinker. Sean was getting older and his visits were now few and far between. We were always glad to welcome him but this time he had some bad news to tell us. He came into the kitchen for a drink and we all sat round the table waiting to hear what he had to say.

"'Tis a terrible thing!" he said. "Over in the west they're having a bad time. I was there just over a week ago. I witnessed it for myself. You can't imagine how bad it is."

We wondered whatever he was going to tell us and waited for him to come to the point. He took a long swig from the drink Mary had given him and then continued.

"It's the tatties," he said. "The whole harvest has gone. People have been relying on the new harvest to see them through the winter and into next year and it's all gone."

We were shocked and amazed.

"What do you mean, Sean?" I said. "Surely they haven't lost the whole crop?"

"Yes," he said, "it's all gone and I saw it with my own eyes. They went to dig the tatties up and they found nothing but black slime. 'Twas the blight, you see, it's ruined the crop for everyone. As I rode from Galway to Clare and down to Limerick, everyone had the same problem. Things started to improve as I came east. I've been warning people all along my route. I say to them 'Dig up your tatties now. Don't wait for the flowers to come on the plants. Dig them up now afore they are afflicted.'"

We were all stunned by the news. Potatoes were the staple diet of so many people. Most people lived in tiny huts on very small patches of land with just enough space to grow potatoes every year. When the potatoes were ripe, they dug them up, stored them in a deep pit and laid hay and turf across the top. They were always able to store enough to see them through the year, although many families ran out after ten months and had to resort to other means for food.

Now, all over the west of Ireland, the potato pits would stay empty and the people would have nothing to eat. Their stomachs would be empty, too. Multitudes of people would be without food. Sean had stopped at one place where a mother and father were trying to pacify their young children who were crying out with hunger. They had been out all morning picking nettles to make a drink for the family. It was all they had but it was a hopeless situation.

"We had a warning about this years ago when a similar thing happened up north," I said to Sean. "It only lasted for one year then and we hoped it wouldn't come again."

Sean remembered this too and said it had been a warning sign which we hadn't taken notice of. But I wondered what could have been done to prevent it happening again. There had been no way of knowing if or when it would come back.

Fortunately, we didn't grow potatoes in great numbers on our farm. However, since I'd taught the school children how to grow them, we did have a small crop. The next day, we were up early and made a start on digging them up. Sean, who had slept overnight in our kitchen, stayed to help us. We had a reasonable crop.

"Sure, they're not full-grown yet," said Sean, "but they're good enough."

We breathed a sigh of relief that our crop hadn't been destroyed. When we were halfway through the digging, I paused and wondered if we should leave the rest and let them ripen fully as normal. Sean argued against this. He said, "If the weather changes overnight and we have wind and rain, there's no telling what will happen."

He said the blight was caused by a fungus which was blown in on the wind or the rain. It could ruin everything in an instant. We continued to dig and filled our two pits. We stored a sack full of seed potatoes in the loft for next year. Jack and Tom helped us. We were all very quiet as we worked. Later, Tom said, "Pa, what will happen to all those poor people?" I told him I didn't know but if there was a God in heaven, he would make sure they would be all right. I sounded as if I believed it but in those difficult times I was not at all certain.

Dick came home from school telling us he'd heard the bad news. People everywhere were talking about it. We told him what we'd done and he asked, "Will the tatties be safe in our pit? All the school children know where our pits are after you gave them lessons on growing potatoes."

I thought about it and said it was a good point. It would be easy for someone to come in at night and take the whole lot away. The next morning, I decided to move the pits far away from the barn where no one could find them. I was up early and found a good spot. They were now out of sight to visitors and in the shade of our old oak tree.

Mary was very worried about the future. She asked me if I thought we would be all right. I told her I hoped so but there was no knowing what would happen in the next few months. I reminded her we had enough livestock and other crops on the farm to sustain us. We were luckier than most and I was sure we would survive.

Sean told us how some of the families in western Ireland lived. He said almost all relied on potatoes for sustenance. It was surprising how many potatoes they ate. A grown man ate anything from 14 to 20 potatoes at one meal and some had two or three meals like this a day. Potatoes were their complete diet. It was amazing to us that this meagre diet kept them going. We had a much more balanced diet ourselves and it was difficult to believe these poor people existed on so little, but it was true.

We were lucky to miss the potato blight but I worried about what would happen in years to come. As the days went on, we heard terrible tales of what was happening in the north and west of the country, with whole families dying of hunger. Every year there was always a month or two when people went hungry while they waited for the potatoes to ripen and they existed on stirabout if they could afford the oats. But now the potato pits had stayed empty for a whole year, not just for a couple of months. All over Ireland stomachs would be empty.

CHAPTER TWENTY-ONE

In the following weeks, we heard terrible tales of the famine which had struck our homeland. In the west of the country, people were up in arms against the landlords' agents who were continuing to export all their grain crops to England, leaving none for the Irish. The agents' main aim was to make money for their masters and they had no feeling for their fellow countrymen. In the north west of the country, men had blockaded the ports and tried to stop the export of grain but the British Army fired shots and dispersed them and the trade went ahead.

Many people used what was left of their rent money to buy food, leaving them with no money to pay their landlords who then evicted them. Countless numbers of people were destitute. Some families fled their homes, using their rent money to pay for their passage out of Ireland to America. Over the following few years, the population declined at a rapid rate, partly due to the amount of deaths caused by famine and partly due to emigration.

One night, I sat in the kitchen with Mary and the family. We discussed how we could make sure we had enough food for the following year. Jack said the farm was more productive now. We were growing wheat and oats which we sold at market. The income from these was used to pay our rent. We discussed whether we could find a grinding facility so we could make flour. Mary said a good stock of flour would see us through difficult months and it would be used to bake bread amongst other things.

I thought about this and wondered how much it would cost to obtain a grinding wheel so we could mill our own flour. I decided to give it more thought. Storing flour and oats would see us through troubled times.

I talked to several local people about grinding corn. In the olden days, farmers used a quern for grinding. I was interested and enquired more about it. Apparently, the quern consisted of two small circular stone wheels, one on top of the other. There was a handle attached to the top stone and corn was placed between the stones. The women in the family would sit and turn the stone with the handle in the top stone until the corn had been ground as fine as they needed it. No one knew if these querns could still be bought and no one knew if there were any still in use in the district. I would have loved to see one but there was no luck to be had there. We didn't know of anyone locally who used this method and couldn't find one for sale.

However, after making several enquiries, I discovered that many farmers in the district took their corn to the mill at Mullinahone. I was amazed to hear this as I didn't know we had a mill so close to home. There were plenty of mills over the border in County Kilkenny where they had fast flowing rivers like the King's River and the River Nore. Using the Kilkenny mills was out of the question as it would involve a long round trip but a mill in Mullinahone, so close to us, would be ideal.

I didn't think there was a river strong enough in Mullinahone to move a mill wheel so I decided we should find out more. A small river flowed through the town but I had never seen the mill. I made enquiries and I was surprised to hear that the mill was a flourishing concern, used by many farmers in the district and I wondered why we had never used it in the past. Da must have been too busy with his cooperage and I suppose he thought that his barrels brought us more money than grinding wheat.

When Jack came in from the fields that evening, I discussed with him the possibility of milling our wheat. He thought it was a good idea. We would have at least two cartloads to take to the mill. If necessary, we could borrow a third cart from one of our neighbours. They would surely agree the loan if they knew they would be reimbursed with some of the flour.

So, we decided to look into the possibility of taking our wheat to the mill. If this worked out well, it would mean we wouldn't have to sell it at market.

One fine day in spring, Jack and I set out to visit the mill. As we approached the town, Jack said, "Have you ever thought about the meaning of the word Mullinahone?" I knew it was derived from the Irish language but it was years since I had studied our native tongue. I looked puzzled but Jack said, "It means 'mill on the river cave.'" I was surprised at his knowledge.

When we arrived in Mullinahone, we saw an old man sitting on a bench. We stopped and asked him if the river was strong enough to support a mill. He laughed and said if the river ran dry, the mill wouldn't work. So far that year the river had been in full flow and there had been no problems. He said he used to work for the miller and pointed us in the direction of the mill which was on the road leading south from the town. We thanked him for the information and went on our way. As we drove through the town, Jack said, "You're right about the river. We just crossed over it. It's quite small."

We continued on our way and soon found the mill. We couldn't miss it. We had never travelled this road before. It was a surprisingly large stone building set on the river bank. We parked our cart outside, tethered our donkey and went in to talk to the miller. It was a much larger operation than I had envisaged. We had a long talk with him and he showed us around. We saw the mill operating to its full capacity. The miller advised us when to come and what we should do. It was all very impressive and I was confident in arranging for all our grinding to be done there in future.

We didn't know the name of the little river but I later found out it was a tributary of the Anner which flowed into the River Suir way down in south Tipperary.

Mary met us when we arrived home. She was pleased to hear of our success and said she'd been thinking of us all morning and wondered how we were getting on.

Meanwhile, news of the failure of the potato crop and the subsequent famine had left a morose atmosphere about the district. Everybody feared their crop would be hit and prayed it would miss them. We and our neighbours were fortunate not to have suffered that year but we all worried about the future. Next year the blight might hit us all. I realised now how important it was to look ahead and prepare for the worst.

One day, Dick said, "Pa, I'd like to do something to help those poor people who are near to starving." I said it was a noble thought but there wasn't anything we could do. There was a famine and we couldn't feed the five thousand. My remark hit a chord with Dick. He was a strong believer and had high religious values but the mention of feeding the five thousand caused him to query his beliefs.

"Pa, how could God do this to innocent people? It's not fair."

I said I didn't have the answer and I'd wondered the same thing myself.

¤

The register of the tithe applotments which had been recorded a few years ago was now overtaken by another survey of land holdings in Ireland. This new survey was called the Griffiths Valuation of Land. We were able to see extracts of the valuation and found the following listings:

Islands – John Frisby, cooper, house, pig house, barn and workshop – 2 acres
Tithe – £1, five shillings and ninepence

Islands – George Frisby (Uncle Thomas' son), house and pig house
Tithe £1 and ten shillings

Modeshill – the Ryan's farm was listed under John's name. I told John he should have his name removed from the list or he might have to pay the tithe.

I was glad to see that the tithe charged to our farm was low in comparison with others and happy that the surveyor had listened to me. Things would of course be different as Jack expanded the farm and we had more productive agricultural land.

Now the list was published, people started to complain about these unfair taxes but we had to pay them. If we didn't, we would be taken to court and fined which would have been even more costly and we might even face eviction.

¤

1847 had proved to be a bad year but we were lucky to survive it without problems. We and our near neighbours were fortunate but the famine did hit one or two families in the surrounding area. Travellers and beggars were also suffering from the shortage of food. Many were starving and soup kitchens were set up in many areas to give these poor people one meal a day. I couldn't imagine our family surviving on just a bowl of soup every day. We were so lucky to still be able to eat well.

In the same year, a cholera epidemic meant even more deaths. A fever hospital was established in Ballingarry. Our doctor, Dr. Fenelly, had been put in charge of the Ballingarry fever hospital and we wondered if this would take him away from his local patients.

We were surprised to hear the fever was now rife in the workhouse in Callan. Times were bad.

CHAPTER TWENTY-TWO

Dick came home from his school in Ballingarry one day with news we didn't want to hear. There were rumours of another uprising. Many young people had heard of nationalist movements on the continent of Europe, in particular in France, which had become a republic after the French Revolution and the young were hoping to achieve the same for Ireland.

These young people were inspired by events in Europe. They hated Daniel O'Connell, the well-known politician, who was trying to form an alliance between Ireland and the British government. They didn't want this. They wanted an Ireland free of the British Empire. They wanted Ireland to have its own parliament and so they formed a group called Young Ireland which denounced anything to do with O'Connell. They preached tolerance, freedom and truth, and had just one goal – an independent Irish nation. They said they would use any means to achieve their aims, provided these means were honourable and reasonable.

We were disturbed to hear this news. Ireland might be better off on its own but we didn't think it could be achieved by rebellion and it looked as if that might happen. We dreaded returning to the rebellious days of our youth. The leaders of Young Ireland said they were principled and good but we could see trouble ahead.

The leaders of the movement, William Smith O'Brien, Thomas Francis Meagher and Richard O'Gorman, had travelled to Paris to see how France had managed to become a republic. Meagher returned to Ireland with a tricolour flag which he said represented the green of Catholic Gaelic Ireland and the orange of Protestant Anglo Ireland. The white in the middle of the flag represented peace between the Catholics and Protestants.

O'Brien had discovered that the revolution on the continent had been relatively bloodless. He preached that he could obtain similar results in Ireland. He wanted to unite Irish landlords and tenants in a protest against British rule. We thought this was a difficult, if not impossible, aim.

All was quiet for a while and little was heard of the movement. But in the summer of 1848, more young people joined Young Ireland. Many blamed the British Government for the famine and said the British could have done more to help feed the hungry Irish. Corn, which would have fed many thousands of people, was still being exported to England by greedy Irish landlords who were filling their coffers. The many deaths from starvation could have been prevented had the British government stopped the export of corn. There was much discontent and with so many hungry and disgruntled people it was not surprising that young people were joining the new movement in their thousands. Fortunately, the famine hadn't reached our quiet corner of the country and all seemed quiet in our district.

Dick told me that several young men from Ballingarry had joined the movement. He told us we must be prepared for trouble ahead. I talked to Mary and we both thought our little backwater at Islands was a safe place to be. We were situated almost a mile from the main road which ran from Mullinahone to Ballingarry but we remembered the occasion when our house was set on fire by a gang of youths and we began to worry.

In July 1848, the government labelled the Young Ireland movement as troublemakers and threatened to imprison the ringleaders. The newspapers said the young men had only two choices: they should either flee the country or they should stand their ground with armed resistance.

Later, we learned that the leader, O'Brien, decided the movement would have to make a stand. We wondered where and when it would be.

Towards the end of July, O'Brien, Meagher and Dillon raised the standard of revolt and travelled from County Wexford through County Kilkenny and into County Tipperary. They made camp on the southern slopes of Slievenamon. We were shocked when we heard they were in our county – this was too close to home. We were very apprehensive and feared for our lives. The movement said they were peaceful but there was no knowing what these angry young men might do. In days gone by, protesters like these stopped at nothing. In those awful days, they had wandered the countryside burning houses, thieving and even raping women. Dick talked to our neighbours and we all agreed to post a look-out at the end of our lane who would warn everyone immediately if they saw trouble coming along the main road.

Sure enough, our worries proved correct. Our look-out rushed back one day, saying a troupe of people carrying large tricolour flags was marching along the main road towards us. He thought they were heading for Ballingarry but there was no knowing which route they would take and we worried they might take a short cut up our laneway.

We hid inside the house and made sure all our doors and windows were closed. We barricaded the doors as we had no locks on them. Normally, our door was always open, so friends and neighbours could call on us at any time. Visitors came and went as they pleased, always knocking on the door before entering. How I wished we could lock our doors! We pulled a large chest against the front door and a table and chairs were wedged against the back door in the kitchen. That would have to do. I sent all the children upstairs and told them to keep quiet and not to look out of the window.

We waited with bated breath. Two, then three hours passed. Eventually, Patrick, our look-out, came and knocked on the door.

"All's clear," he said. "They've passed the end of our lane and gone up the main road towards The Commons and Ballingarry." We all heaved a sigh of relief. For the moment, we were safe. I called up to the children. "You can come down now." We moved the barricades and gradually life got back to normal. It was very frightening.

Later, we heard what had happened in Ballingarry. O'Brien and his supporters had all met at The Commons. His supporters consisted of many local people, miners, tradesmen and small farmers. This mass of people barricaded themselves near the coal mine, hoping O'Brien would not be arrested. The Callan police had been alerted and were on their way to take O'Brien. The rebels waited for the army and the police to arrive.

The police from Callan drew near to The Commons. They saw barricades in front of them, behind which milled a huge mob of people. They quickly realised they would not be able to tackle such a large crowd; they were outnumbered. So, they moved off in a different direction. The rebels followed them, taking a short cut by running across the fields. The rabble were catching up with them so the police and the militia took refuge in a farmhouse. The police barricaded themselves inside the farmhouse and pointed their guns out of the windows, having taken the children of the house as hostages. The rebels surrounded the house and there was a deadlock.

The lady who lived in the farmhouse stood with the rabble and pleaded with the police to let her see her children but they refused her request and refused to release the children. The lady was desperate to get them out and pleaded with O'Brien to help her. She tried to negotiate with the police through a window, without any luck. One of the rebels tried to plead for her; he told them if they gave up their guns, they would be free to go. But they refused him, too. Someone fired a shot from the window and all hell broke loose, with each side firing on each other. Many, including O'Brien, were wounded. The pitched battle went on for many hours and several men on the rebel side were shot.

The rebels finally gave in and dispersed when they saw another detachment of police arriving who had been called out from another town. Once they were defeated, they quickly scattered. The siege was over.

It was incredible that this happened so close to home. We hoped it might be the end of Young Ireland. The ringleaders were eventually arrested and convicted of treason. They were among the last people in Ireland sentenced 'to be hung, drawn and quartered.' They were kept in prison until the fateful day arrived but luckily, at the insistence of Queen Victoria who thought the sentences were too harsh for the crime committed, they were reprieved and transported to Australia.

When we heard what had happened to these young men, we breathed a sigh of relief. The uprising was talked about in the neighbourhood for many months. Ballingarry is only three miles away from our house so we had a lucky escape. We always thought we were out of harm's way living in the country but this event had shown us we were not as safe as we had thought. They were troubled times and we couldn't help wondering if this sort of uprising might happen again. I decided it was time to put bolts and locks on our back and front doors. We were glad Da and Mam hadn't lived long enough to see the year of the Great Uprising or to see the terrible results of the famine.

People still talked about the Young Ireland movement. We remembered how frightened we were when we heard the rebels were less than a mile away from us as they marched up the main road towards Ballingarry and were glad that episode was over. But memories of the uprising made us wary of strangers. Gradually, things began to settle down and we all looked forward to a safer future for our families and, hopefully, a more peaceful time.

¤

But things were not going to settle down quickly. We soon heard rumours of many Tipperary men camping out on Ahenny Hill near the Ahenny slate quarries. News came to us that the peasantry had gathered there, and were drilled daily, all armed with pikes and rifles. Neighbouring farmers were sympathetic and supplied them with provisions so they didn't go hungry. All was quiet and everyone waited to see what would happen.

In September, when we thought everything had quietened down, a group of men from the Ahenny Hill gathering made their way to the Ahenny Police Station. The police, warned that they were coming, made their escape just minutes before they arrived and took refuge at Piltown. The rabble took possession of the police station and eventually set it on fire, reducing it to ashes. All autumn long, other police stations in the area were attacked. Police left their stations and went to Clonmel and Carrick for safety. Luckily there were no police stations near us but we never knew where their next attack would be.

Ahenny Hill was not far from Windgap where the Killamery Frisbys lived. We worried about them but later heard they were safe. I also hoped that Thomas Frisby who lived in Ahenny had not been involved.

Rumours also came to us about bands of rebels hiding out in the Wicklow Hills. No one knew when or where they would be making trouble.

While the British had such a control over our country, there would always be rebels; we would not be at peace until we were free from them. We didn't know how we would achieve this so we did nothing. For the sake of peace, my family didn't get involved with political movements. We hoped our children would follow our example and live a quiet life, believing that eventually the future would be better.

¤

Following the failure of the Young Ireland movement, many tenant farmers turned to more peaceable means of protest, such as joining Tenant Protection Societies which fought for fair rents. Societies had sprung up in Callan, Mullinahone and Ballingarry. People thought rents should be adjusted to take into consideration the fall in productive crops such as the potato. If people could afford their rents, there would be fewer evictions. Tenant movements were set up in many parts of the country and helped people who were struggling to pay their way.

CHAPTER TWENTY-THREE

Peace soon returned to the countryside and the time arrived for us to get the harvest in again. We contacted the miller and booked a slot for our milling. The whole family was ready to help in the fields.

Harvest time was always dependent on a good spell of dry weather. As soon as we approached the season, Jack made sure we had enough helpers. This year, he had arranged for some neighbouring boys to join us, so we were quite a big crowd.

Everything was set fair for a bumper harvest and after the last few worrying years we thought we deserved it.

We all gathered in the wheat field. Jack was the scythe man and he was the first to start. We all watched as he swung the scythe from side to side, cutting the wheat as he went. The wheat fell on the ground behind him. We were soon given the signal to start work, following behind Jack, working in pairs and gathering the wheat into bundles. Behind us came others who bound our bundles into sheaves, tying them up with straw. Finally, the last two men picked up the sheaves and stacked them into stooks.

Jack had to stop every so often to sharpen his scythe. He said it was the most important part of harvesting. Nothing could be achieved with a blunt scythe. I think he was glad of a short rest to get his breath back. It was hard work and everyone had their part to play. The sun was hot on our backs as we worked.

Meanwhile, Tom was working on the other side of the field, swinging his scythe like Jack. He had his own band of followers who were collecting the wheat for him. Jack was an expert and by noon had already cut twice as much as Tom. Jack said Tom was doing very well for a beginner. Without him, we wouldn't complete the cutting in one day. It was back-breaking work and Tom couldn't be expected to do more. Jack was full of praise for his contribution.

The best part of the day was when Mary and Mikey went back to the house to bring out lunch for the workers. Tom went to help them and brought out a barrel of cider. We all sat around, chatting as we ate bread and cheese, washed down by cider. Mary had made a new batch of barnbrack which was everyone's favourite. It had never tasted so good. It was wonderful, enjoying the food in the sunshine after a hard morning's work. But it was soon back to work.

At the end of the day, we left the stooks in the field for the wheat to dry. In a few days they would be ready for loading on to the cart to be taken to be threshed. It was critical that good weather continued for a few days for the drying process to be complete. Then, after a day or two, we all went out again to gather up the stooks and load them on the cart. We took them to our barn where the threshing took place, separating the wheat ears from the stalks. The stalks would be used in the coming winter, providing feed and bedding for the animals, and the wheat ears were destined for the mill.

After the threshing, Jack had one more job to do – the winnowing. He always waited for a windy day as it made the job much easier. Basically, winnowing separated the wheat from the chaff. The wheat ears were collected together in buckets and the contents thrown on to a large canvas sheet. As the wheat landed on the canvas, the chaff was blown away in the wind. When we were sure as much chaff as possible had been removed, the wheat ears were bundled up in sacks ready for the mill.

The last job to be done, when all the stooks had been taken in from the field, was the raking up of all loose stalks of wheat left behind. When all of these had been gathered, Mikey let the chickens out in the field to pick up any corn left on the ground. They were so happy – all that lovely grain to gobble up.

We had just two cartloads of wheat to take to the mill and we set out very early one morning for Mullinahone. I drove our cart, and Jack and Tom followed close behind. We arrived at the mill at nine o'clock and the miller said the flour would be ready for us in 24 hours.

The next day, we went back to the mill to collect our corn. The miller greeted us.

"Come in. Your order is almost ready."

We stepped inside and witnessed the very last of our flour flying down a chute into sacks.

"That was well timed!" Jack said.

We hadn't expected to see the mill in operation. I thanked the miller and paid him while Jack bundled the sacks on to our carts. I was relieved that we wouldn't go hungry in the months ahead. Half our load was sufficient for our own needs and we set aside the other half for market. I had a good night's sleep after another busy day.

A week or so later, Jack and Tom started to prepare the land for next year's harvest. Together they worked the land with our old plough attached to our donkey and Jack walked him slowly through the field. Tom followed behind, clearing weeds and stones out of the furrows. This was back-breaking work and took place over several weeks. Jack liked to have it finished before winter set in, as the frost would help to break up the large lumps of soil.

¤

Jack's young son, Richard, had recently joined us at my school and was proving to be a good student. He had been well schooled at Modeshill before he came to live with us. He was quite a character and a very independent little chap. In a few years, he would be joined by his sister Catherine.

For a long time, I had thought that the Irish tradition of naming children was not very helpful. Children were named after parents and grandparents so names continued through the generations. We then had three Richards in the family: myself, my son, Dick, and now

Jack's son. We also had three Catherines. I was glad we called our daughter Kate so she couldn't be confused with Jack's wife or with their baby daughter. I supposed all families had this problem.

¤

Meanwhile, many people were still suffering from the famine. We were lucky the potato blight hadn't hit us and fortunate we had a good food stock. The British government still refused to stop the export of Irish grain. If grain was available in our shops, it would have reduced the number of people dying from hunger. Some said it might even have prevented the famine. It seemed to us the British thought we were not worthy of assistance from them. The greedy British landlords continued to export their grain crops.

In England, Sir Robert Peel had arranged for America to send consignments of Indian corn to Ireland, which came from the maize plant – a poor substitute for wheat corn. People complained that it was stale, with a musty smell, as it had not been ground properly. It led to many people suffering with stomach pains, but, with nothing else available, there was no other choice but it did little to solve the problem and it came too late.

Many people had no money to pay their rent. The landlords were unforgiving and there were many evictions. We heard horrific tales of families being evicted, following which their home was set on fire so there was no chance of return. Thousands were made homeless in that way and now wandered the countryside, looking for help. Some died on the wayside. It was tragic.

Another problem brought about by the famine was the vast number of dead bodies. People were dying not only from starvation but also from diseases like cholera and typhoid. Mortuaries and doctors were struggling to keep pace with the limitless number of bodies. The sheer numbers led to delays and therefore to decomposition of the bodies before funerals could be arranged, leading in turn to infection, with the additional problem of being attacked by wild animals.

In 1846, the government introduced the Coroners Act, which sought to overcome some of these problems. The Act stipulated that all dead bodies should be taken to public houses for safe-keeping. Most pubs had beer cellars which were cold, ideal places to store bodies which were kept there until an inquest could be held. Publicans who refused to accept these bodies were subject to large fines.

Dick still pestered me, asking if there was anything he could do to help these poor, hungry people. I was proud of him and his charitable thoughts. He had a very sensitive nature and I could see he was suffering at the plight of these destitute people. I wished there was something I could suggest to help him. He still taught in Ballingarry but I knew he was not completely fulfilled. However, there was little I could do for him.

¤

Jack and Catherine were both very happy since their move to Islands and Mary loved having them in the house with us. When she was not helping me in the school, she cared for young John, Catherine and Bridget to give Catherine a break. The children reminded her of the old days when her own family home rang with the laughter of little children.

Catherine and Jack's children were the first of many grandchildren and the house was filled with their happy laughter for years to come. I looked forward to all our children coming to my school.

¤

Jack's son Richard was still far ahead of the other children and he showed a great interest in religious studies. In years to come, if he wanted, he could have a great career either in business or even in the church. Dick suggested Richard would learn more if he moved to the school in Ballingarry. There wasn't much more I could teach him so I thought this was a good idea as he would receive a broader education there. Dick told him he would be able to study extra subjects like geography, history, and even Latin and Greek. He was thrilled to hear this and he pestered his father to let him go to Dick's school. He knew he would enjoy the extra lessons in religious studies, just like his uncle.

In time, Jack agreed to let Richard change schools. We were sorry to lose him but we soon noticed a big difference in him. He was a very serious young boy and changing schools was the best thing for him. He was happier to be with boys of a similar standard as he had been held back in my school being so far ahead of the other children. He was now in the right class for his age and he enjoyed the company of the other boys.

Jack and Catherine saw the birth of their fifth child, Margaret, in 1851. Catherine had a much easier birth than she had with her first children.

CHAPTER TWENTY-FOUR

For most of my life, poverty had stalked Ireland. The potato famine did untold damage to our country and we still heard tales from Sean the tinker of food shortages, of people still suffering and begging for money to pay for their next meal. Soup kitchens were still operating in many towns. A meal of soup was like manna from heaven. Destitute people now ended up in the workhouse, which was overcrowded, leading to miserable conditions for everyone.

Like many others, our first instinct was to make sure our own family didn't suffer in those trying times but many people endured horrific conditions for a second year as the potato blight continued. Again, there was limited failure of the crop in our district but we were amongst the fortunate few. Sometimes, we felt guilty at our good fortune but there was little we could do to help the poor. We had a large family to feed and we were already contributing by paying the Poor Tax.

By 1852, the potato crops had fully recovered but the damage had been done. Estimates varied but it was believed that as many as one million men, women and children had perished during the famine. Another one million managed to escape poverty and starvation by emigrating overseas.

¤

In the same year, one of the worst storms ever known hit the area. The storm raged for several days; rain poured down and everything was waterlogged. On the second day, we heard large claps of thunder followed by lightning and hailstones. My big fear was the little river just over the road from the house although it had never overflowed in all the time the family had lived at Islands. But now the water level was rising fast and I worried our house would be flooded.

The river had now become a torrent. We watched it rise hour by the hour and it spilled over on to the road, the nearest it had come to the house in living memory. There was a slight slope on the road so the water flowed down the road away from us and I hoped it would continue to flow that way. But if the river rose a few more inches, I knew it would be at our front door. We watched in horror as we barricaded the front door with furniture though of course this wouldn't stop the water flowing in.

The water was dark and muddy. From its source, far away up in the Tipperary hills, it flowed through the countryside and picked up mud and dirt on its way. It was so dirty we wouldn't be able to use this water for washing ourselves as we had done for so many years as it would take several weeks for the muddy water to disappear and give way to the lovely clear water we were used to. It meant extra trips to the pump, where we normally only ever went for drinking and cooking water but now we had to go there for all our water needs.

We went to bed that night but didn't sleep well. The wind whistled round the house and the rain hammered on the windows. I tossed and turned and couldn't sleep. Mary was the same. At three o'clock I got up and went downstairs and found Jack there. We were both very worried and donned our overcoats, put on our boots and opened the front door. What we saw amazed us – the river had encroached so far it was actually lapping on our front doorstep. It would not be long before the water was seeping into the house and we had no way of stopping it.

Barricading the door the previous evening had done little to help. We racked our brains and came up with the idea of nailing planks of wood across the doorway. Jack went out to the barn and came back with several planks under his arm, and a large bag of nails and a hammer in his hand. As he hammered the planks in place, I helped him by holding one end and eventually we had nailed enough planks to reach a height of about three feet. It wasn't perfect but it was better than nothing and was the best we could do.

The hammering woke the rest of the family and they were now all standing on the stairs in their nightshirts, wondering what was happening. I showed them what we had done and said there was nothing more we could do.

"It would be better if you all went back to bed. You'll be safer upstairs but I don't think you'll get much sleep."

At six o'clock we looked out of the parlour window and noticed water was lapping half-way up our planks on the outside but fortunately it had not forced its way in. We worried now that it might rise to the top of the planks as if it did, it would spill over into the house.

The awful muddy water began to seep through at the edges of the door. We grabbed several old blankets, sheets and rags and tried to breach the tiny gaps. Water has a way of finding its own level and there was little we could do to stop it. We realised we were fighting a losing battle so decided to wait and see what our fate would be. We went into the kitchen and made a hot drink and sat there, considering our next move. We had not had any sleep that night and we were both very tired.

If the worst came to the worst, the water might make its way into our little kitchen. Two hours later, when this hadn't happened, we went outside again to investigate. We were horrified to see that our little hallway was about two inches deep in filthy muddy water so we went into the parlour again and looked out of the window. To our amazement, we saw the water was receding very slightly and hadn't reached the top of the barricade. We heaved a sigh of relief. If ever it happened again, we would have to be ready for it.

The rest of the family were up very early, carrying their shoes as they splashed through the hallway on their way to the kitchen. The talk was all about the weather and the flood. Over breakfast, we decided our priority was to check on our neighbours and make sure all was well with them.

Fortunately, none of the neighbours had suffered as we had, but, like us, they had all been kept awake by the fierce winds and the lashing rain. After finding they were all right, we set about cleaning up our mess. There was nothing worse than muddy water in your house and I can't describe how awful it was.

To add insult to injury, there was no clean water available to clear up the mess. It took several days of hard work to get the house back to normal but we thanked our lucky stars the flood hadn't done more damage.

After breakfast, Jack went out into the fields to see the effect of the storm there. He was distraught. Our wheat crop, which hadn't yet grown to its full height, had been flattened overnight. There was little we could do to salvage it. We were glad we had continued our annual trips to the mill in Mullinahone and had plenty of flour in stock. This year we wouldn't be going to the mill as we had nothing to take. Jack hoped we could salvage some of the beaten down stalks to use as fodder but we didn't look forward to collecting it in.

The gale raged on for several days. High winds and torrential rain battered everything in its wake. The failure of our crop was bad enough but the worst thing was the damage the storm had done to our thatched roof. Part of the roof, which had been mended several years ago after the fire, seemed to have been torn apart. When the raging winds died down, Jack climbed the ladder to examine it.

When he came down, I knew from the expression on his face it was bad news.

"The whole roof has been affected. It looks as if we'll have to have a completely new roof."

This was very serious but I remembered Da's bank account. Although a new roof would be expensive, we would be able to afford it but this was something we would have to sort out quickly. We didn't want the inside of the house to suffer from the wet weather.

We decided to replace the thatch with slates. We could buy the slate from the quarries in Ahenny, which wasn't far away. I went to see a builder in Mullinahone and asked him to quote for a replacement roof and he came the next day to inspect it.

He gave the roof a complete survey and agreed slate would be best. I told him I could buy slates from the Ahenny quarries and asked if this would save money. He agreed it would and said he would tell us how many to order. His quote would be for the removal and disposal of the thatch, and replacement with slates. I was quite happy to do the ordering as I knew Thomas Frisby would give me a good price.

The builder made one proviso: he had not been able to see if the roof joists were in good order. If any needed replacing, it would incur an extra cost. He couldn't see these until all the thatch had been removed. He said he would send the quote in a day or two but in the meantime, he offered to send round a couple of workmen to cover the void so we wouldn't suffer from any more water leakages.

In a few days, his quote arrived. It was much lower than I expected so I asked him to start work as soon as he could. Jack and I went over to Ahenny to see Thomas Frisby and place our order for slates which would be delivered to us in ten days' time.

We were very pleased when the roof was finished. We didn't have to pay extra for new joists – they were all in good condition. Mary and I went into Callan to draw cash to pay the builder. On the way home, I said to Mary, "Well, that's made a dent in Da's money but, thankfully, there is still plenty left."

"Da was saving up for a rainy day! He didn't know how rainy it would be!" Mary said. We laughed. I was sad Da was not with us to see how useful his money had been.

¤

The house looked very smart with its new slate roof. We decided to lime wash the walls to smarten up the outside. Uncle Thomas' son,

George, agreed to do this for us. He finished off the job by painting our window frames. The house looked as good as new and I was very satisfied with the outcome of a bad experience.

CHAPTER TWENTY-FIVE

Tenant farmers were still protesting about unfair rents. Peaceable protests were held in many parts of the country and farmers sought a guarantee of the tenure of the land they held.

In 1850, the Tenants' Rights Association held a meeting in Ballingarry. To everyone's surprise, about 20,000 people turned up for this meeting. Ballingarry had never had so many visitors! Tenant farmers had come from far and wide, from all over County Tipperary, to hear the speakers. The meeting was held in the open air and fortunately the weather was good.

I decided to go to the meeting but Jack said he was too busy. I found it difficult to hear the speakers above the rabble so I left early. I noticed the police were there in force. They were clearly expecting trouble from such a large crowd. There was no trouble while I was there but we heard later that the police eventually had to disperse the gathering by firing on them. It had been essentially a peaceful event so this action was not popular. I was glad I had left early. Many people were troubled by the unnecessary and cavalier attitude of the police.

¤

Following the famine and the general economic situation in the country, there were many bankrupt landlords in Ireland now because of unpaid rents. In the 1850s, we began to see the sale of these lands which were now called Encumbered Estates. Many people suddenly found themselves with a new landlord who had bought the land they lived on. We were lucky as our landlord hadn't sold his lands.

My cousin, David Frisby in Ballyduggan, was worried. His land holdings at Ballyduggan and Kylaglass were to be auctioned in an Encumbered Estates Sale. He was worried the new landlord might terminate his lease. He and Catherine now had many children and David had always looked forward to his children taking over the farm when he was older. Now it looked as if his dream might not come true. David had worked hard on his land and made many improvements. He hated the idea of giving it up. The auction of David's lands was to be held in Dublin and he asked me if I would like to go up to Dublin to the sale with him. He was anxious to know who his new landlord would be.

I had never travelled far from Islands. In fact, Kilkenny town and Thurles were the furthest I had been. The prospect of visiting our capital city appealed to me and Mary encouraged me to go. She said it would be a good experience for me to see how the sales work and to spend some time in Dublin.

The sale was on 12th January 1855. I left Islands early in the morning and walked to David's farm. From there, one of his sons took us to Kells to catch the Bianconi coach to Dublin. The coach driver was the same man who had brought me back from Carrick all those years ago after Granma's funeral. He was looking much older and said he was retiring at the end of the year. He said he would be glad to give up work and spend more time with his family.

We had a comfortable trip and arrived in Dublin in the early evening where we found a lodging house for the night. After settling in, we went out to get something to eat. We eventually ended up in a pub near the quayside. This was a wonderful experience for me! I wasn't used to pub life and had only been in a pub on very few occasions. These waterfront pubs in Dublin were full of life and many bars lined the streets. Music from fiddles or accordions spilled out into the streets, and people talked and laughed while they drank their porter. Occasionally, someone got up and sang a folk song and I thoroughly enjoyed the evening. Just after 11 o'clock, we made our way back to our lodging house.

The next day, we were up at the crack of dawn and, after breakfast, found our way to Henrietta Street where the court was. We were early and had an hour to wait. The courtroom filled up quickly and there was a lot of interest in the sale. The auction covered all the tenancies in David's landlord's estate in the Mullinahone area. When the auction was over, David went to talk to the man who had bought the land he lived on. He introduced himself, telling the man which lands he held. The man was actually an agent for the new landlord. David asked him what his situation would be now, with the new landlord. He was told all existing leases would be honoured which was what he wanted to hear but he was still worried as his lease was on a one-year rolling basis. However, he was happy for the time being.

The visit to Dublin was a good experience. The sale finished in the late afternoon and there was no way of getting home that evening. As a result, we had another night on the town. It was amazing to see how the other half lived. I enjoyed the visit but I was glad to get home the next day, to our quiet part of the country. I told Mary all about our experiences. She wanted to know how secure David's lease was so I told her he was all right for 12 months but didn't know what would happen after that. Many leases were written like that and rolled on year after year, provided the tenant paid his rent regularly. We both hoped all would be well and that David's lease would renew annually without any trouble.

The campaign for land law reform continued and became the focal point in Irish politics over the next few years. There was intensive campaigning by the Land League which had three aims: fair rents, freedom of sale and fixity of tenure. But these would be a long time coming. David was going to join the Land League as, above all else, fixity of tenure was uppermost in his mind.

¤

In the last few years, Jack had doubled his efforts on our farm which, in spite of the potato famine, had become quite productive.

He visited many fairs and livestock sales, either buying or selling. He had a good head on him for figures and we were doing well. He had sold our first barley and oats crops at auction. Although he had stopped growing potatoes, he had planted turnips in one of our smaller fields which were for our own consumption. Everything in excess of our needs was either fed to the cattle or went to market.

We saw an increase in our income when Jack sold the first cattle he had reared on the farm. These fetched £7 a head. He also sold lambs but these only fetched 11 shillings a head. He kept the ewes for rearing next year's lambs. We had to pay a shearer once a year and when we sold the wool, it brought a small profit.

Jack had recently decided to rear piglets and sell these at market. So, this year our pig would be rearing her young meaning there would be no pig killing … and no new football for the boys.

Young Mikey and Tom still helped on the farm. Tom was involved with the cattle and sheep and also helped with the crops. Since Jack expanded the number of cattle on the farm, we now had a glut of milk so Mikey was now making butter, and sometimes cheese, in our small dairy, which we then started to sell. He also looked after the chickens, bringing eggs into the kitchen for Catherine. Excess eggs were sold to neighbours.

Many years ago, Da had planted an apple tree which was now providing large crops each year. We had a pit to store the apples and so we had a plentiful supply all year round. All in all, I was happy with the way the family had taken to farming and I wished Da could have seen how well we had progressed. I also wished he could have seen how all his grandchildren had taken to their duties. He would have been proud of the way Jack was running the farm. I knew he would be saddened that we had closed the cooperage business but I was sure he would have understood this. More than anything, he would have been pleased at the way the house looked with its new roof and the paint work which cousin George had done for us.

¤

I was now 64 years old and feeling very tired. Teaching had taken a lot out of me and I had decided it was time to retire. Mary was pleased about this – she thought I'd been looking exhausted lately and decided I needed a rest. I told her I was going to close the school down but would continue my scribe work which brought in small amounts of money and took up very little of my time.

Mary wondered if there was any way we could keep the school running. I told her that there was no one to take over from me so it had to close. We were both saddened by this as it had been a large part of our lives. In fact, if we hadn't had the school, Mary and I would never have met! But all good things must come to an end. We comforted ourselves with the thought that a large number of young children now had better prospects for their future life and we were looking forward to spending more leisure time together and with our family.

We decided to tell the family of my decision to retire on my 65th birthday. This seemed to be a good time to close the school. When the day arrived, all the family were invited for a small party to celebrate. They drank a toast to me and I thanked them. Now was my opportunity to tell them about our plans. Surprisingly, they were not well received. The family had never thought the school would end. I told them it wouldn't be long before the government opened a new national school in the district and our school would be redundant. The family was not happy and the occasion turned out to be very sober when it should have been happy. I wished afterwards I had chosen a different time to tell them this news.

The next day, Dick came to me and asked if we could have a talk. He said he had gained valuable experience as a teacher in Ballingarry and thought he was well qualified to take over our little school. He didn't want me to close it and asked me to consider his proposal. He said he would do everything he could to make it a success. He hoped I would agree with him.

I had always thought Dick was well established at the Ballingarry school and I never thought he would want to take on this responsibility. I was pleased he wanted to do it and I asked him to let me have a few days to think about it. He thanked me and looked forward to hearing my decision.

I discussed it with Mary and she was as surprised as I had been, but nevertheless pleased. She thought it was in everyone's interests to let Dick do this. The one stumbling block was how much we could pay him. The school income was so small I doubted we could match his earnings in Ballingarry. The next day, I did some sums and came up with a wage for him. I hoped he would accept it. I decided to talk to him about it in a few days' time.

The next weekend, I had another chat with Dick. I asked him if he was still keen to take over the school.

"Yes, I would love to," he said.

I told him about the financial situation, telling him how many paying pupils we had and what the annual income was. I suggested the wage we could pay him and he was happy with the figure – he said it was the same as he was earning at Ballingarry!

"When can I start?" he said.

So that was that. He would be taking over when he'd worked out his notice at Ballingarry and I would be free of my duties. I told him if he ever wanted help, I would always be there for him, but I knew he would want to make a go of it on his own.

¤

The day came when uncle Thomas, and their boys were due to set off on their journey to America. Then we heard that Uncle Thomas, and Aunt Nellie would not now be going with the family. They had been advised they might be refused entry on account of their ages. This was a great shame as they had made so many plans for their future. However, their children were still keen to go. Thomas and Nellie decided to travel with them to Cork to see them off on the ship. They had decided they would then return to live in Carrick-on-Suir.

The family had packed their few belongings into bags. They decided not to take too much luggage with them. We were all very sorry to see them go. We all stood at our front gate watching them load their luggage onto the large cart which Jack had borrowed from a neighbour.

Jack was taking them to the train for Cork, which stopped at a railway junction near Thurles. There had been a lot of excitement in the district when the Dublin to Cork railway had been built in 1844, particularly when we knew how close the railway came to us – just 15 miles away.

Thomas had purchased boat and train tickets from a local agent in Ballingarry.

The boys would sail from Cork's Queenstown harbour, previously known as Cobh, re-named after Queen Victoria's historic visit in 1849. They were very excited at the prospect, not only the journey but also the chance of a new life in America.

Mary was in tears as we waved them goodbye. I was sad too and wished them good luck in their future lives. When the cart disappeared from view, we all went back into the house. Dick said how strange it was now the little house next door was empty. He hadn't realised that Thomas' son, George, had decided not to go with his parents and would be staying on in their little home.

¤

As soon as Dick had taken over from me at the school, I turned my attention to another matter which had bothered me for some time. I had been writing this book for many years, following the life and times of the Frisby family. The time had now come to hand over to a younger member of the family to continue it for me.

Mary and I had a long chat about this. We both agreed that Dick should be asked to take it on. Jack didn't have the same literary skills as Dick but it was too soon to land it on Dick as he had only just moved jobs. So, we left it in abeyance for a while and decided to leave the decision for a few weeks.

Eventually, I talked to Dick and asked him if he would like to take over the book from me. He said that although he would love to do it, he couldn't give it the time it deserved. He asked me if I could wait a while until he was settled in school. Jack overheard our conversation and was worried that if Dick didn't do it, I might ask him.

"I think Dick should do it," said Jack. "He's a man of letters – not like me, I'm just a farmer."

Dick heaved a sigh and, looking at Jack, said, "I will do it as soon as I'm sorted at school. I'll be glad to take it on. It's important that father's work is continued. He's done a wonderful job and we must keep it going."

So, I was glad that Dick had agreed to it. Jack had huge responsibilities on the farm and I knew he didn't have the time to do it. I also knew I wouldn't be happy with the results if he had offered to do it as he simply wasn't suited to writing.

I turned to Dick.

"I'm pleased you want to do it; how about I carry it on for a few more months just to give you time to get yourself sorted out in school? You can take it on when you're ready."

Dick agreed and said it was a good idea.

"Yes, that's fine. I'll be happy with that."

¤

I must now say goodbye to you, my readers, as I pass you over to my son, Dick. It was a pleasure writing for you and I hope you enjoyed reading this and will continue to do so. Mary and I are looking forward to our retirement and we hope to have several years of peace and happiness.

PART TWO

CHAPTER TWENTY-SIX

Hello, I'm another Richard. They call me Dick. Not only did I take over my uncle's school, I also took over his book. My uncle has delegated me to continue our family story. I hope I can follow in my uncle's footsteps and do a good job for him and for you.

¤

When I took over our little school at Islands, it was late in the year 1853. We had an excellent first term with 48 pupils attending. Forty of these were fee-paying so the school was now paying its way. Among them, of course, were family members, my nieces and nephews receiving a free education.

All was going well but in early 1854, bad news came our way. The Education Board announced they would be opening a new national school in Mohober.

We were surprised to hear this as Mohober is a small place and far from any big centre of habitation. Mohober is our neighbouring townland and just up the road from Islands. In fact, it's within easy walking distance from home. They intended to take over the house of a farmer who had recently died. It would make an ideal schoolroom. Plans were underway to open it in the autumn. All they had to do was make good the premises and find a teacher and enrol the pupils.

I was devastated by this news. I ran a good school but I thought many parents would prefer a national school and the advantages it had to offer. So, it looked as if I would be losing pupils. I didn't know yet what the advantages of the new school would be but it was supported by the Department of Education and the Catholic Church so it would attract many parents. If the new school was given enough publicity, it would surely be a success. We had discussed this in the family and were all surprised it was being set up so soon and that it was so close to us. Many new national schools had been opened in larger towns but rural areas like ours had been poorly supported. The family were very upset and we didn't know what would become of our little school which I had thought was a great opportunity for me and one I would be running for years.

But it was not to be and just as I thought, the new school opened. Pupils were already gradually drifting away from me. If one member of a family went, their brothers and sisters followed. Other youngsters went because they wanted to be with their friends who had already left us. It wasn't long before I had just 15 pupils left, and half of these were family members. My school was not sustainable at this level and sadly we had to consider its closure.

I was very unsettled and refused to send our children to the new school so I continued to teach them myself. This had its benefits: I was able to give more time to each student and the results I obtained confirmed my thoughts. I was pleased that our children were ahead of others of their age.

But I didn't feel completely fulfilled. I knew that keeping the school running was only a short-term measure. As soon as they were old enough, the pupils would leave to make their way in the world. There'd be no new children coming through to take their places. I became worried and depressed and found it difficult to continue writing, but I did my best.

One day, I decided to pay a visit to the new school in Mohober. As Mohober is the next townland to ours, it's only a short walk away. In fact, you can almost see the school from our upstairs windows.

I was surprised at the number of pupils there – far more than I ever had in my school. The teacher was a young man called Pat Maher. I listened outside before going in. The children were very noisy and boisterous – there didn't seem to be much discipline or learning taking place.

I knocked on the school door and a young boy opened it. He looked at me quizzically.

"What do you want?" he asked. I told him I wanted to speak to Mr. Maher. He told me to wait a minute and shut the door in my face! I heard the teacher shouting at the children and telling them to be quiet which I think was for my benefit. After a few minutes, he came to the door and asked me what I wanted. I introduced myself and told him I was a teacher. His response was, "There aren't any jobs here, sorry." I explained to him that I hadn't come for a job.

"I'm a neighbour and just interested to see how you are getting on."

"Fair enough," was his abrupt response. He had obviously decided not to ask me in and I didn't want to waste any more of my time there, so I bade him farewell and went on my way.

That evening, I told my brother Jack about my visit to the school. I told him I wasn't impressed.

"I didn't have the opportunity to gauge his ability as a teacher," I said. "But he's very young to have such a responsibility and there doesn't seem to be much discipline."

Jack said he had come to the same conclusion after talking to neighbours. Everyone thought Pat Maher was too young and inexperienced.

My visit to the new school had depressed me. This young man had such an opportunity – he had twice as many pupils as I had ever had. Everything was laid on for him by the Department of Education but he was too young to realise the great opportunity that lay in front of him. He could make Mohober a great school but his heart wasn't in teaching and I wondered if he had had any previous experience.

Not much, I thought, going by his age and from what I had seen and heard.

Just one year later, Pat Maher left Mohober school. I wasn't surprised. His place was taken by another young man called Hamilton Bell. I was glad to hear he was of a higher calibre and hoped the school might now be more successful.

Over the next few years, my depression didn't lift. The family worried about me but they could do little to help me. I was well and truly down in the dumps and found pleasure in nothing.

In 1855, young Richard, my nephew – Jack's first son – turned 17 years of age. He was still at school in Ballingarry but was due to leave the following year. We wondered what he would do in his future life. He could have been an ideal assistant to me if our school had continued, but that was not to be. We all noticed he was very committed to the Catholic Church; he helped the priest during Mass and assisted with other church activities. Richard wasn't suited to farm work and it was going to be difficult to find another occupation to suit him. We thought teaching was an option for him but there weren't any opportunities locally.

We were very concerned about young Richard's future. We knew he had ability and we didn't want to see it wasted. We found ourselves going round and round in circles discussing the problem.

"I do wish life was simpler," I said to Jack. "We won't have the same worry with your other children. None of them show the same abilities as Richard. Hopefully, your boys will take to farming and the girls will all get married and have families of their own to look after."

Richard left school in 1856 and apart from the work he did for the church, he was at a loose end. I often talked with him about what he would like to do now but he was always evasive and our talks never reached a conclusion. Many young boys in the neighbourhood had formed gangs and the older ones seemed to be frequenting public houses. Like Richard, they had no work and were at a loose end. We were glad he wasn't involved with them – their life style was the road to ruin – but that didn't stop us worrying about his future.

One day, my aunt Mary suggested the basket making business might be an opportunity for Richard. She wanted to slow down and hand over to someone younger. We didn't think it would be a long-term job for Richard and we wondered if it would suit him but we thought it would occupy him until he decided what he wanted to do. It would give him some responsibility and fill some of his days. He would have to deal with the lady workers and finished baskets would have to be taken to market. If he wanted, he could even set up his own market stall to sell them. In the past we had always sold them to a stallholder. With his own stall and no middlemen involved, Richard would be able to make more profit. I thought this was a good idea and I discussed it with Jack. Jack was keen to see his son involved in something and thought it was worth trying.

The following week, Jack asked Richard if he would like to take over the small business from his aunt Mary who wanted to retire. At first, Jack was dubious.

"I don't know anything about it. Why me? Am I suited to this work?"

Jack told him his aunt would show him the ropes and if he gave it a try, he would soon know whether it suited him or not. He explained he could run it as a business and he would have to keep accounts and pay the workers. Jack told Richard he was not being forced into doing it. Richard agreed to give it a go.

So, he joined his aunt in the little business and they worked well together.

"Well, that's it," Aunt Mary announced one day. "I'm now officially retired."

I was amazed at how quickly this had happened but I was glad for her. Richard had taken full control of the business. He had a good rapport with the ladies who did the basket making. They called every morning to collect the reeds to make the baskets at home. I soon noticed he was spending a lot of time with a young girl called Mary

Corcoran and I wondered if anything would come of their friendship.

All seemed to be going well for him, but you never know what is, just around the corner and, in early 1860, we were astonished by the news Richard brought home.

It was a Sunday and Richard had been helping at church. Everyone was at lunch when he came home with a broad smile on his face.

"What do you think the priest announced today?" he said.

We had no idea and waited to hear what he had to say.

"They're calling for young men to go to Italy to fight for the Pope in the Papal Army. The Pope is defending his lands against a dictator called Garibaldi. They want all able young men to go to his assistance. This is just what I've been waiting for! If we go, we'll be in the Irish Brigade and they'll pay our passage to Italy and provide us with uniforms. When the fighting is over, they'll pay our passage home, or to anywhere in the world we might want to go. This is an opportunity I can't miss! Isn't that wonderful news?"

We were all amazed. We didn't think this was good news at all. We didn't want Richard going off abroad to fight in another country even though he would be fighting for the Pope and the Papal States. We worried he might get killed in battle.

"You might think it's a wonderful opportunity, son, but you haven't thought it through," said Jack. "You are a young man with no idea about what it's like to go into battle. You have no experience. I'm going to put my foot down and I won't let you go. Forget this silly idea. Remember your family and how anxious we will all be. It's a madcap idea. You're only 20 years old and you can't be running off abroad to fight other people's battles for them."

"Father, I've thought it through and I *will* be going. You can't stop me. I will soon be 21 and I can do what I like. But I would rather go with your blessing."

Jack was surprised at his son's attitude.

"We'll leave it for now and speak about it tomorrow. I want to talk to the priest and ask him for more details."

The next day, Jack went to see the priest to find out more and when he came home, he told us that all priests in the country were calling on young men to go to Italy to fight for the Pope. The Pope was defending the Papal States against Garibaldi who wanted to make all of Italy Protestant by turning the whole of Italy into a republic.

The Papal States were in the middle of the Italian peninsula and stretched across the whole of the country, from Rome to the eastern coast. Garibaldi needed to take control of these lands to achieve his aims. The Pope was defending his lands and he hoped for the help of a young army drawn from all parts of Europe.

Jack told the priest he was unhappy with his son going off to fight someone else's war. The priest replied, "If we're true Catholics, it's our war too! Pope Pius has called out for all Catholics to support him. It's my duty to encourage as many young men as possible to join the Irish Brigade. You, as a Catholic, should welcome this."

Jack loved his son but felt defeated. There was little he could do to argue against such passion. We are all good practicing Catholics but he thought the line had to be drawn somewhere. He couldn't agree that young Irish men should fight for a cause in another country.

Jack hoped Catherine would have a suggestion to stop Richard going. Maybe he would listen to his mother. There was a very subdued atmosphere in the house that evening.

Nothing more was said about Richard's plan to go to Italy and all was quiet for a few days. But Richard hadn't given up on the idea of joining the Irish Brigade. He visited the priest and told him he wanted to be included, even though his family were against him going, and he asked him not to send any messages to him at home. He would keep in touch on a daily basis.

Richard took his uncle Mikey into his confidence. Mikey wished he was younger as he would have loved to go with Richard to fight for the Pope. At first, Richard was careful not to tell him too much. He asked him if he could keep a secret.

"Of course I can!" Mikey said. Richard told him he wanted someone in the family to know what he was doing, as he couldn't talk to his mother or his father about it.

"Mikey, I want to tell you all about the arrangements I'm making. Please keep these to yourself."

After hearing Richard's plans, Mikey said he wouldn't utter a word to anybody until Richard was well away from the house.

A day or two later, Richard confirmed to Mikey that he was definitely going to Italy. He said he would go quietly when the time came. Once he had gone, Mikey would be free to tell the family everything.

"It's a shame I can't tell them myself. I don't like keeping secrets but I know you agree I have no alternative."

Mikey agreed again not to say anything until Richard was well away from the house.

A few days later, Jack noticed Richard wasn't at breakfast. He assumed he was late getting up and thought no more of it. Jack went off into the fields as usual. He came home later that day for his evening meal and when Richard didn't turn up for supper, he turned to Catherine.

"Where's Richard?"

She replied she hadn't seen him all day. Mikey decided the time had come to tell the family what had happened. He looked a little awkward when he made his announcement.

"I know where he is." Falteringly, poor Mikey told everyone what had happened. "Richard left the house in the middle of the night, taking with him a sack containing a few belongings."

"Where's he gone?" asked Jack.

"He asked me not to tell you until he was well away. It's now several hours since he left. He went to the railway station in Clonmel. He's gone to join the Irish Brigade to fight for the Pope in Italy."

Well, a bomb could have hit the house. Jack was irate and shouted all sorts of terrible things about Richard. Most of all, he was cross with the priest and said he had no right to encourage young men in this way. He said it would be a fool's errand. He was sure Richard wouldn't even survive the journey and even if he did arrive safely, he would probably die in battle.

The whole family was hushed and quiet while Jack ranted and raved. Even when he stopped shouting, nobody said anything. The room had gone silent and nobody dared to speak. Gradually, as they finished their supper, each member of the family disappeared and they all kept out of Jack's way.

The children were very upset as they had never heard so much shouting in the house. Young Catherine started to cry and her mother took her out into the garden and some of the family followed her. You could cut the atmosphere in the house with a knife and they all wished they were somewhere else.

When they had left, I was alone with Jack.

"What would you do?" he asked me. I said I was as surprised as he was but I couldn't offer any helpful suggestions.

I thought about it for a while and then said, "Do you remember when we were his age? I wanted to do something to help people. I remember feeling useless as I couldn't help those worse off than myself. I know how Richard feels. He wants to make a difference and it's not unusual for young men to have these feelings."

Jack glared at me. "He's not your son, so you can't possibly know how I feel."

"We're all very surprised at what's happened. It will take a long time to get over this."

After a while, Jack's wife Catherine joined us. She put her hand on Jack's shoulder and said, "We're all devastated by this, Jack, but there's nothing we can do now. We must just accept that Richard has gone. He wanted to go and nothing would have stopped him. He's doing what he wanted to do. He'll be 21 years old next month and we'll have no hold over him. He's now a young man and must answer to himself for his actions. We are helpless and there is nothing we can do. We must move on with our lives."

Jack looked surprised at Catherine's outburst. It wasn't like her to have her say. He turned to her and said, "I don't think I'll ever get over this. He knew I was against it and he's gone against me. Well, it's time for me to bring the animals in for the night. Standing here complaining won't get the work done." He turned and walked out of the back door, slamming it behind him.

Catherine looked at me and we both raised our eyebrows and said no more.

Time was of the essence in sending these young men to Italy and the Catholic bishops and priests had set up a well-oiled machine to enable their flock to take part in the war. Priests were kept informed of all movements. Eventually, we discovered that Richard was told he was to be included in a small group of young men and was given seven days' notice of his day of departure.

The day of Richard's departure arrived. He had to get to Clonmel railway station by three o'clock in the afternoon. A group of young men from all over Tipperary and neighbouring counties gathered there and were met by John Walsh, a brother of the Catholic curate of the town. Mr. Walsh had all the necessary papers to enable the young men to travel. He gave them through travel tickets to England and on to the continent of Europe.

A week or two after Richard had gone, Jack decided to buy newspapers to find out what was happening in Italy. He read that the Papal Army had already assembled to defend the Papal States and many young Irish men had gone to Italy. The papers were full of this news. The British government was against young Irish men travelling to fight overseas. However, there was no law to stop them going and the Catholic church supported them and helped them on their way.

Arrangements had been made by the Church with the Railway Companies for through tickets from Ireland and on to the continent. Their final destination was Ancona in Italy, a port on the Adriatic on the eastern side of the country. The young men would be needed for possibly up to four years and would be paid an immediate sum of nearly £20, and afterwards a bounty of four shillings a day. As soon as they were no longer needed in Italy, they would be guaranteed a passage home or anywhere in the world they wanted to go.

The police were instructed by the government to keep an eye open for any suspicious movements which might indicate a young man heading to join the army in Italy. Even though they kept close observations, we didn't hear of any arrests. We suspected that as most of the police were themselves Catholics, they had sympathies with the young men and turned a blind eye to their movements.

On the 16th May, a few weeks after the young men had gone, the government issued a notice forbidding foreign enlistment. This only led to increased numbers of young men joining up to fight and young volunteers were assembling in towns and villages all over Ireland. The Foreign Enlistment Act forbade the recruitment of British subjects to fight for foreign heads of state but there were loopholes and many of the Irish travelled accompanied by priests. They stated on their passport applications that they were travelling as pilgrims. Others said they were travelling to look for work, thereby circumventing the new Act.

Later, in July that year, the government was still concerned about the increase in the number of young men who had left Ireland that summer. The Attorney General received a list of 1132 passports which had been issued in May and June. Various destinations were stated on their passports, the most popular ones being the Continent of Europe, Italy and Rome. But once they had left the country, the government could do nothing. Richard would have had a passport – without this he couldn't have travelled.

The newspapers carried many stories about the Pope's war. Catholic priests criticised the authorities for interfering in people's right to travel. They said that these young men were keen to assist and should be helped. The Church thought it shouldn't be necessary for them to declare on their passport application the purpose of their travel or their destination. The government said the young men had acted unlawfully but they didn't have enough evidence to prosecute them. As far as the authorities were concerned, it was too late to act. The matter was eventually forgotten and it was hoped the young men would not be arrested when they returned home, if indeed they did come home.

But the matter was not forgotten in our household. A few weeks after Richard left, we were all talking openly about him and wondering how he was getting on. Jack was the only member of the family who refused to discuss the matter. But one day he came to me and said, "I just wish I knew he was all right. I pray for his safety every night. Every day I wait, hoping a letter will come from him."

But in those first few weeks nothing arrived.

CHAPTER TWENTY-SEVEN

The weeks went by and still we heard nothing from Richard. Jack and Catherine had by now given up all hope of hearing from their son. Jack filled his days by working hard in the fields and Catherine had plenty to keep her busy in the house.

One day we heard that the Kelly family in Ballingarry had received a letter from Italy from their son Dan. It had been written just a week after the boys arrived there and had taken over a month to arrive. Jack became hopeful that Richard had written too and maybe his letter would arrive any day.

Two days later, Jack received a letter with an Italian postage stamp. It was addressed to Mr. and Mrs. J Frisby. He picked up the letter and went to show it to Catherine. They sat down together in the kitchen where Jack opened it and started reading it to Catherine. His voice was very low and, try as we might, we couldn't hear what he was saying. Jack and Catherine were engrossed. It was a long letter and we waited to hear the news. When Jack got to the end of the letter he said, "Well, at least he's arrived safely. Hopefully, he's still alive. Let's hope he stays out of trouble." Catherine smiled at Jack. They were both greatly relieved to hear from their son.

Later, Jack showed the letter to the rest of the family. Richard had written it about a week after his arrival in Italy.

Dear Mother and Father,

Well, here I am in Italy. I must apologise to you for the way I left home. I knew you would stop me if I told you I was going. I didn't want a scene with you so I decided it was best to go while you were all asleep. I hope in time you will find it in your hearts to forgive me.

I hope you haven't been angry with Uncle Mikey for keeping my secret. I made him promise not to tell anyone until I was well away. Please forgive me for that too and say sorry to him for me. I realise I put him in a difficult position.

The journey here was long and tiring. I've never been so exhausted and anxious.

We left Clonmel by train which took us to Waterford. We were escorted by Mr. Walsh but he left us at the boat in Waterford. We boarded a boat called The Adonis at midnight, en route for England. From England we sailed to Belgium and there we caught a train which took us all the way to Italy. Mr. Walsh had purchased through tickets for us so we didn't have to worry about the train fares. I am with a good group of young lads. We are all from similar backgrounds.

We have been here now for a few days. So far, it's been very quiet and there is no sign of a war. We were promised uniforms but these haven't appeared. So, we are still in the clothes we left home in. We look a raggle taggle bunch. I hope the uniforms come soon. We were also told we would be issued with guns but so far, no sign of these.

I hope you realise my main reason for being here is religious. Talking to the other lads, I found most had the same motive but there are one or two who just look upon it as an adventure. Some said they had run away from home because they didn't have a job and were bored with life. But whatever our reason for coming, it has been a great experience for all of us. None of us had left home before.

The weather here is very warm. July is one of the hottest months in Italy.

We are camped just outside the town of Ancona and we are waiting to be called.

I hope you are all well at home. I send my love to you all and I will write again when I have more news.

Your son,
Richard

We were all pleased Richard had arrived safely in Italy but we hoped in our hearts that he wouldn't be involved in heavy fighting and we prayed for his safe return home.

The family all talked about the contents of Richard's letter. I looked up his journey in the school atlas and traced his likely path from Clonmel to Ancona, mapping out his journey on paper. I wanted to show it to my pupils at their next lesson. I had yet to calculate how many miles Richard had travelled.

When Richard left home, he left the basket making business in good order. Aunt Mary had stepped back in and picked up the reins so all was now running smoothly. We didn't want her lumbered with it forever so I talked to Mikey and asked him if he was interested in taking it over. Surprisingly, he liked this suggestion and said he would be glad to have an indoor job. When the weather was good he didn't mind being outside but, in the winter, working on the farm played havoc with his chest. He said he would fit this in with his other duties.

We heard from Richard again about six weeks after his first letter. Jack and Catherine were very pleased to learn that he had not yet been into battle.

Dear Mother and Father,

We have now been here almost six weeks and recently we were fortunate as the Austrian Army gave us some of their old uniforms. We all look much better now even though they are a bit tatty. I don't think we'll ever get the new uniforms we were promised by the Italians. Things have moved on and a small group from our section were sent to a place called Spoleto where the battle was raging.

I was not selected to go in this first group so I have not yet gone into battle. I'm still in Ancona and we are told there will be a battle here within the next week or so. We have been drilling and practising shooting in preparation. Please don't be worried. I will do all I can to keep safe. But I must play my part.

It is still very hot here and I wish we had much lighter clothes. The uniforms are very heavy – I think they must be the Austrians' old winter uniforms used to keep them warm in the Alps. They are far too hot for this heatwave.

I hope everything is all right with you at home and I send my love. We understand the Papal Armies are not doing so well. If that continues, perhaps we will soon be on our way home. I have enjoyed the experience but I long to see you all again.

My love to everyone
Your son, Richard

Jack and Catherine were glad to read that Richard hadn't been involved in battle. It sounded as if he was beginning to feel homesick and it seemed as if the Papal Armies might be retreating. If so, it wouldn't be long before he returned home and we all prayed for his safe return.

¤

Mikey was making a good job of his new task with the basket making and he was now left to run it on his own. He was pleased to be working indoors now the winter months were closing in. Jack had arranged for our cousin George Frisby to help with the milking and with other dairy work so Mikey could concentrate on the baskets.

Writing this book is good for me. I miss the challenge of teaching a large group of children. Our little school at Islands now only caters for the children of our family as all the other pupils have drifted away to the Mohober school. It is easy and fulfilling teaching a small group in spite of the big age range. My oldest pupil is Jack's daughter Catherine who is now 12 years old. Her sister Bridget is two years younger and her young brother John just five years old. Our own three children are about the same ages as Jack's. Also, there is Mikey's son. So, in all I am teaching ten children.

We would soon have to consider sending all the children to Mohober School. Fortunately, we had enough money to afford the fees. Apart from the Thurles school, we'd never had to pay for education so it would come as a shock at first. We decided to send the children gradually, starting with the two oldest, Catherine and her sister Bridget. The others would go later when they were ten years old, but it wouldn't be long before they were all at Mohober School and I would be out of work.

My uncle Richard, who ran the school before me, was very busy in his retirement. He still did his scribe work so writing took up a lot of his time. Most evenings he was locked away in the parlour with one of our neighbours who wanted him to write a letter. It was surprising how often people now required his services. I didn't know how people managed before they had a scribe! Uncle Richard and I dreamed of the future when all people would be able to write their own letters but this could only happen when education was opened up to the masses. Life was going to be very different in future.

CHAPTER TWENTY-EIGHT

Now that the number of my pupils was decreasing rapidly, I decided it was definitely time to wind down from full-time teaching. I was still only in my early fifties yet it was surprising how I suffered from aches and pains. I got tired easily and I was looking forward to an easier life. It amazed me the number of hours I'd spent standing in front of a class which definitely had an effect on my body. When I retired, I'd be glad to sit down and occupy myself with another pastime.

My uncle suggested I might like to take over some of his scribe work when I finished teaching and I looked forward to this quieter life.

My brother Jack still ran the farm and he had given no indication of wanting to retire. He loved being outside in the open air and it would be years before he gave up. He enjoyed going to market and buying and selling and he loved to haggle. These visits helped him keep in touch with prices and local news. He had many friends amongst the local farmers and Da's old customers.

We had three local markets: at Ballingarry, Mullinahone and Callan. At all of these the landowners charged a toll on the head of cattle sold in the cattle sales. One shilling was charged for each cow sold on their fairground. It was a lot to pay and it reduced our profit margin. Jack favoured the Mullinahone fair for cattle sales. On many occasions, he had sold an animal before going into the fairground, thus avoiding the costly toll. On his way to the fair, he sometimes met a buyer who offered him a good price. Many potential buyers waited around on the streets approaching the fairground and were prepared to make a bargain on the spot. When a price was agreed, a shake of hands sealed the deal and no toll was paid. A lot of dealing was done in this way.

Ballingarry was the best fair for selling butter, eggs and piglets. Every July, a gooseberry fair was held at Ballingarry and was well-attended. Cartloads of gooseberries were on sale at the fair and we all looked forward to this annual event.

A big attraction at the gooseberry fair was the sports day. The sporting events varied from running races to jumping competitions. A hurling team came from another village to play against our team. The children looked forward to this fair eagerly every year. Our own children were old enough now to take an interest in these sports. It was a tradition which had survived over the centuries. At the fair, men took part in their sports and prided themselves on their physical strength. We enjoyed watching the strong men of the neighbourhood competing in the tug of war, weight throwing, wrestling and boxing.

This fair had not always been so peaceful. Years ago, before the sports were introduced, fights took place between neighbouring parishes called faction fights. The young men of the parish joined their faction and swore an oath of allegiance to fight to defend their village till death.

These faction fights took place all over southern Ireland in Counties Tipperary, Kilkenny, Waterford and Limerick, to name just a few. The young men armed themselves with blackthorn sticks which had been fashioned into cudgels and also carried pockets full of stones to use against the enemy. During the fight, many young men were injured and went home bloodied but satisfied they had fought for their townland.

In other parts of the country, faction fighting was called 'stick fighting' and the cudgels were called shillelaghs. It was a dangerous sport and sometimes lethal. Men fought not only for their survival but also to maintain the reputation of their families and their village.

Sometimes hundreds of men were involved. When I heard stories about these fights, I could never understand where all this anger came from. But I realised we had been a fortunate family and did not have the same deprivations as others. The fights took place in troubled times and I supposed it was a way of letting off steam!

Many years ago, a disturbance happened after the gooseberry fair at a dance that was held in Mohober. All was going well until a fight started between the two factions called the Caravats and the Shanavests. These factions came from neighbouring districts. One young man was fatally injured and died of his wounds. The man who struck the fatal blow was caught and the women at the dance were called as witnesses to a court in Wexford. The guilty man was imprisoned. Injuries and death had followed many of these fights in the past but this one killing put an end to faction fighting in Ballingarry. Instead, we now competed with rival parishes in races and sports. These serious fights were the forerunner of today's strong man sports, such as wrestling and boxing.

Another game played between townlands and parishes was Gaelic football which took the place of the old faction fights. There were no rules and it was a very rough game. Any number of men made up a team but each team had to have the same number of players. At the start of the game, the ball was thrown in the air and, from then on, it was a free for all. There were injuries, but none so bad as the deaths and injuries incurred in previous years. The winner of the game was the team who took the ball home.

Thankfully, all is peaceful at current gooseberry fairs.

¤

We had a shock the other day when Jack's son, John, who was playing with his friends, fell out of a tree. He stumbled into the house crying and holding his arm. Aunt Mary looked at it and said, "Oh, deary, deary me – it looks like he's broken it." When John heard this, he was terrified and started to scream. He was in great pain.

"Shush, now, shush!" said Mary. "We can't have you crying like a baby. You'll set all the others off." John whimpered and said, "Sorry, Aunt, but it really hurts." Mary sat him on a chair and gave him a mug of milk to drink.

We'd never had a problem like this before. I wondered what we should do. Jack came in from the fields to see what all the fuss was about. He lifted John up and sat him on the kitchen table and inspected his arm.

"Now, calm down, son. It looks as if your arm might be broken. We must call the bonesetter. Does anyone know where he lives?" No one knew what to do. Aunt Mary decided to go and see the handywoman, Maureen. She put on her cloak and rushed out to find her. She came back ten minutes later, panting and saying, "Maureen's been in touch with the bonesetter. His name is Patrick and he'll be with us in a few hours."

After tea, we all sat around waiting for the bonesetter to arrive. Poor John was still in great pain and sat by the fire nursing his arm. I didn't know what the bonesetter would do. I wondered how much we would have to pay him. He came at seven o'clock and as he walked in, he said, "Well what have we here? What have you been doing, young man?"

"I fell out of a tree, sir. It hurts so badly. I've never had such awful pain. Can you help me?"

"Well, let's have a look at it. Let's lie you down on the table."

Jack helped John climb back onto the table. John laid down and had difficulty resting his arm alongside his body. The bonesetter gently held his arm, talking quietly to him all the time. This seemed to calm young John down. We were in the background listening and we wondered what was happening as we couldn't hear what the bonesetter was saying. After a while, he turned to Jack and said, "I'm going to have to sort your son out. I'm going to reset the bone for him. Fortunately, he's young and at his age the bones are still growing. They are like sticks and don't snap completely. It's a bit like breaking a twig or a branch of a young sapling. It's called a greenstick fracture. If we support it well, it should grow back as it was before."

This was all new to us.

We all looked on, hoping Patrick could help young John. He seemed to know what he was doing. As he worked, he chatted quietly to John taking his mind off the process. I watched him work and his hands seemed like magic as they moved gently on John's arm. It was a form of massage and he was feeling the broken bone through the skin. I'd never seen this process before and I was mystified. The rest of the family all watched on too. The massage went on for nearly half an hour. Patrick seemed to be in a trance but it was obvious he knew what he was doing. John had quietened down and was more relaxed.

"Good lad, you've been a brave soldier. I'm now going to put a splint on your arm to hold everything in place," the bonesetter said to John.

He took a splint and some bandages from his bag. He placed the splint against John's arm and proceeded to wrap the bandages around it. When he had finished, he helped John to sit up.

"In the next few weeks, you must be very careful and not move your arm too much. I'm going to put your arm in a sling and you must keep it on at all times, even when you go to bed. The pain will gradually lessen and your bone will knit together and in time you'll forget it ever happened. Your arm will be as good as new. For the next two weeks, you must take life very quietly. I suggest you stay indoors and don't go running about outside. I'll come and see you in two weeks' time and I might be able to remove the sling. Let's hope the break will heal quickly."

Jack thanked Patrick and helped John down off the table. He turned to Patrick and said, "Thank you so much. What do we owe you?"

"Well," said Patrick. "I don't charge a set fee. It's up to you if you want to pay me. I'll be quite happy if you give me a couple of shillings. That will cover not only this visit but also any subsequent visits."

"That's grand," said Jack. "We're very grateful to you. Before you go, will you take a glass of cider with us?"

As Jack and Patrick sat drinking their cider, Jack asked, "How long have you been working as a bonesetter?"

"That's a long story," said Patrick. "My father and my grandfather and many generations before have all been bonesetters. From an early age, I watched my father carry on his trade. When I was old enough, I was apprenticed to him and I went with him on his many visits around the county. These visits were a valuable education for me. My family are blacksmiths so when we are not setting bones, we are working in our foundry. But helping others is a reward in itself. There is nothing better than to see people back to full health when their bones have mended. It's a good life."

John took it easy for the next two weeks. I sat with him and helped him with his reading. When I was busy in school, his Aunt Mary helped him and his reading came on in leaps and bounds.

Patrick came back in two weeks and removed John's sling. He massaged the arm again in the area of the break.

"Good. I'm very pleased. It seems to be healing well. It's not completely better yet and it may take another few weeks. I'll put the sling back on and you must keep it on for another week and after that you can start using your arm very gently. However, if you are in any pain, ask your father or your mother to put the sling back on and call for me. I don't think it will be necessary but I mention it just in case."

After Patrick had sorted John out, Jack said, "We're just about to have our evening meal. Will you stay and eat with us?" Patrick stayed and over the meal told the family some tales about the bones he had set. All sorts of stories came out. He said that most accidents happen when young children are playing outdoors. But he had also helped people who had been thrown from their horses; another common injury was caused by people falling when getting in or out of their carriages.

"Accidents will happen. People are careless. They rush about, thinking they are infallible but a slip soon tells them otherwise. We're glad when we're called to help. As I said before, there's nothing better than seeing people when they're mended."

Thankfully, John's arm healed quickly. He was soon out and about again with his friends. This was a lesson to us. We realised how vulnerable we were, living out in the country. We were fortunate to have people like Patrick the bonesetter and Maureen the handywoman to help us. Our family had lived there for well over half a century and were lucky to have them at times of crisis.

I hoped life at Islands would continue as before but times were changing. I often thought about how life would be in the future. Changes had come partly as a result of education. Young people were beginning to realise there was a big world out there and some of them wanted to go out and explore it. Not many boys were happy now to settle for a life on the farm and girls didn't want to work as scullery maids in big houses. I could see a time in the future when young people wouldn't stay at home and would move away to make a living. We were fortunate as our family had been stable for such a long time. The great famine had been all around us but we didn't suffer. When illnesses like cholera were running high and there were riots in big towns, they didn't seem to touch our neighbourhood. We had been lucky to live in a fairly safe district and life had held few surprises. But none of us knew what the future would hold.

CHAPTER TWENTY-NINE

It was a long time since Jack had heard from Richard. He and Catherine still worried about him. They wanted to know how he was faring. It was nearly two years since his second letter and they wondered if he would ever come home.

One day, in 1862, young John came rushing into the house, shouting.

"Come out everybody! Come and see who's coming up the lane!"

He rushed back out to the lane and called again for the family to join him. Everyone wondered what was happening and we ran out of the house to see what was going on. Soon all the family were in the lane. We looked into the distance and saw a lone figure walking towards us.

"Look, look!" shouted someone. "It's Richard! He's come home."

Everyone was outside and the children started jumping up and down with excitement. Jack was the only one missing – he was still out in the fields and Mikey rushed to find him.

Jack arrived and hugged Catherine.

"I never thought we'd see this day. The prodigal son returns!" Jack said.

As Richard drew near, we could see how tired and weary he was. The children were very excited and ran to meet him. It was a scene of joy and they jumped up and down with excitement and hugged him. When they had quietened down, Richard was reunited with his parents. Jack and Catherine couldn't believe he'd come home safely.

"Let's get you inside," said Jack. "You look tired and dirty. You've lost weight. When did you last shave? How long have you been travelling?"

"I've been travelling since I left Italy about three weeks ago. I've been on the go virtually non-stop. I'll tell you all about my journey when I've cleaned myself up and had something to eat. Mother, I can't wait for a taste of your wonderful food. I've hardly eaten for three days. Let's all go inside and when I'm settled, I'll tell you my story."

This was a joyous day for our family. We had almost given up hope of ever seeing Richard again. There was much excitement and the children were rushing around in circles and whooping with joy. Everyone was looking forward to hearing Richard's story.

Jack went into the house and made sure there was plenty of water warming up over the fire in the kitchen. He went to the shed and pulled out the old bathtub then called upstairs to Richard.

"Come down, son. I have the bath ready for you out in the back."

Richard came down and was soon in the bathtub with everyone crowded round. Jack scrubbed him clean with soap. It was just like old times! Richard relaxed in the bath and said, "I've never felt so good and it's wonderful to see you all. I'm so happy to be home!"

After he had dressed in his old clothes, he joined us at supper. Everyone was asking him questions and wanted to hear his news.

"One at a time. Give the lad a chance, he's only just arrived. Let him tell us his tale in his own time," Jack said.

And so, Richard began to tell us about his trip. He started by telling us about his journey to Italy. In the beginning, they had travelled on the ship Adonis from Waterford to England. Then, they crossed the English Channel by boat to Belgium and from there they journeyed by train through France and on to Italy. He described to us the town of Ancona where he was finally based.

"We arrived in July and the weather was hot. It was always warm in Italy and none of us were used to it. At first, we slept in tents and there were 12 men in our tent. Can you imagine the smell? They were big bell tents but inside they were smaller than our bedrooms upstairs. We were all hot and sweaty but we soon got used to the stench. There was nowhere else to sleep. Just imagine, 12 men in one of our bedrooms and you'll understand how squashed we were.

"We slept on canvas groundsheets. We could have slept outside as the weather stayed warm through the night but we were frightened as there was a danger of roaming wild animals. Wolves and wild boars had been seen in the area. We had to put up with these conditions and we continued to sleep under canvas. Then, after a couple of weeks, we were moved into the Lazzaretto barracks at the edge of the city. We were much more comfortable there and slept in proper beds.

"Soon, about 150 of our comrades were sent to assist in a battle in Spoleto. The battle went well but we never saw these young men again and we wondered what happened to them. We were told they had joined another unit.

"Then, another group fought in the battle of Perugia. I was still stuck in Ancona in the hot sticky weather, wondering if I would ever see any action. It was not long before my time came, in September, when we defended the town in the battle of Ancona. It was a rout. We were beaten. The enemy had better equipment than us and were well organised. They were bombarding us from both land and sea. After several hours of fighting, our commander realised we were not going to win and, to avoid further bloodshed, he raised the white flag of surrender on the city walls.

"We had put up a defiant response to the enemy and were lucky not to get killed. I thank God to this day for saving me. I lost several of my new friends who were killed in battle. I will never forget my time in Italy.

"We were taken prisoner after the battle and we wondered what our fate would be. The Italians bundled us onto a train and took us to the city of Genoa in northern Italy where we were put in prison to await our fate. We didn't know what to expect. We were in prison for several weeks and were not allowed out so we suffered badly. But our officers were held in a separate place and were allowed out in the town. No such freedom for us!

"The Italians didn't know what to do with us and eventually decided to send us home. They put us on a boat to Marseilles in the South of France and from there we were at a loose end. We had to find our own way home. A group of us travelled by train to Paris and from there to the port of Le Havre and then it was just a boat crossing to England.

"When we arrived in England, it was as if we had come home but we still had a long way to go. It was wonderful to hear people talking in English, our own language, at last. Even though it's summer, we had to get used to the cooler weather.

"We took another train to Liverpool where we caught the boat to Dublin. This was a long sea journey, much longer than the English Channel crossing. We were on one of those new steam ships, in bad weather, and it took nearly six hours to reach Dublin. You can imagine my feelings when I set foot in Ireland! It was amazing to hear people speaking with the Irish accent – music to my ears! In Dublin I said goodbye to my new friends as we split up to go our different ways home.

"I had just a few pence left when I arrived in Dublin – enough to buy some food. I bought a loaf of bread and some cheese. That was the best meal I had for months. I had no money so I couldn't catch a coach home. The only alternative was to walk. Yes, I've just walked all the way home. When I arrived at the outskirts of Dublin, I could see green fields and green trees all around me – so different to the parched dry earth of Italy. I was so glad to be here. It's a long walk from Dublin to Islands and it took me seven days. I was so tired and I wondered if I would ever make it but I soldiered on. At night, I slept in churches or barns. Two priests listened to my story and asked me in, gave me a bed for the night and made sure I had something to eat.

"Can you imagine how I felt when I turned into our lane and

started the long walk up to Islands? And then I saw you all in the distance! I've never been so tired and so dirty but so happy in all my life. It's wonderful to be home. I love you all!"

CHAPTER THIRTY

Richard took a while to settle back at home. The first night, he slept for nearly twelve hours and Jack told the family to give him space to recover. It was several weeks before he was fully recuperated. But then he was at a loose end and didn't know what to do with himself. I was still teaching some infants who were too young to go to Mohober and suggested he might like to help me. He was a good teacher and I was soon able to leave him on his own with the children.

Jack was glad to see his son occupied again. One day, he said to me, "I'm glad Richard has taken to teaching. But I worry what he'll do when the children move on to Mohober."

I told him not to worry, that Richard was good at his job and would have no trouble finding work. The experience he was gaining was good for him. After the events of the past few years, he probably wasn't ready yet to go out into the world of work. We agreed he appeared to be fine but it would take some time for him to get over the horrors of war. Jack thought he might be worrying unnecessarily and the matter wasn't mentioned again.

¤

In 1862, the lease on our house and land was sold by our landlord through the Landed Estates Court. It was a huge sale which encompassed many landholdings in several local townlands, including ours. The sale was similar to the one I had attended in Dublin with cousin David a few years ago. Our lease was in Jack's name and I asked him if he wanted to go to the sale.

"I don't see the purpose of going all the way to Dublin. What will be, will be!" Jack said. He appeared very laid back about the whole affair. I couldn't understand why he appeared so uninterested. He turned to me and said, "Do you remember when cousin David went to Dublin?"

"Yes, if you remember I went with him."

"And what became of that?" said Jack. "Nothing. Everything will go on as before. It will just be a change of name at the head of the lease – a new landlord. There's nothing we can do about it. The sale covers many properties in this area. I don't think all the tenants are going to be evicted from their homes at the same time, so no, I'm not worried about this and I won't be going."

The sale took place on the 8th July. As Jack prophesied, our lives didn't change and I needn't have worried. I wished I had the same attitude. If I had, I wouldn't lose so much sleep. I had restless nights for several days before the sale, just worrying about it. Jack laughed at me and said, "I don't know, Richard. If we did everything your way, we'd be out of house and home through worrying."

¤

In 1864, we heard that the teacher at Mohober School was leaving. There were all sorts of rumours flying around the neighbourhood about him. Some said he had been reported to the Department of Education but we didn't know why. He might be leaving of his own accord but in any event, his departure was swift. Straight away, I thought this would be an ideal opening for Richard. I didn't mention it to anyone but I was hoping he would hear of the vacancy and would apply.

It was not long before we discovered that Richard had indeed applied to the school. At first, he didn't tell us as he was worried he might not get the job. He didn't want us to be upset if he wasn't successful. But, one day he heard he was being considered for the post and he couldn't control his excitement as he told us his news. He had to wait another two weeks for the final result.

In 1865, Richard was appointed as head teacher at Mohober School. We were all delighted and celebrated with him. For me, this was the icing on the cake. My father had run a hedge school which was against the law and many young people were educated by him. In due course, I had taken over his school from him. When the laws changed, my school was recognised in the neighbourhood. Finally, my nephew Richard took over from me. Now we had the good news of his appointment to Mohober School. For three generations, we had educated not only our own family but also our neighbours' children. I was very proud that Richard was now head of a national school.

In the following years, Richard became a valuable asset to the community. He was respected by all. He threw himself into teaching but was still very keen on religious studies and included half an hour of religious instruction every day. On Sundays, he still helped the priest at Mass. Jack wondered if his son would ever get married but he seemed to be happy leading a bachelor life. School and his pupils meant everything to him.

In 1872, I noticed Richard was spending time with a girl, Mary Corcoran, who had helped in the basket making. I knew they had been friendly, many years ago, before he went to Italy. Now it seemed they had renewed their friendship. They started walking out together and it was obvious they were fond of each other.

¤

While Mary and I were leading a much quieter life since I gave up teaching, my brother Jack was still working on the farm. But in recent years he had slowed down and reduced his workload. Like me, he felt old age creeping up on him. He still loved being out in the fresh air but couldn't cope with a large workload as he once did. We still had the pig, chickens and enough cows to provide us with milk. Most of our cattle had been sold off. Also, we had a very small flock of sheep. With the exception of the wheat field, our other fields now lay fallow again. We still enjoyed harvest time particularly when the weather was good and we still all lent a hand with this.

Jack was at his happiest when the baby lambs were being born in the spring! Sometimes a ewe died or was unable to feed her young and he had great pleasure in bringing the newly born lambs into the kitchen and keeping them warm in a blanket in an old cardboard box by the fire. He fed them from a milk bottle. The children loved lambing time too and always wanted to help feed the motherless young lambs.

CHAPTER THIRTY-ONE

Richard married Mary Corcoran in 1874. When Richard returned from Italy, their bond had grown greater every day but for several years he had concentrated on his new job at Mohober School. Marriage was the last thing on his mind. But, when the time came, it just seemed natural for them to get married. Poor Mary had been waiting for such a long time. We were all pleased to see her so happy now.

Richard came to see me one day. I asked him how things were with him as I'd noticed how tired he was looking.

"I hope you are not overworking in your new job."

"No. Our life is good and I'm very happy teaching at Mohober. I just have one problem and I hope you'll let me share it with you."

"Of course, what is it?" I replied.

He looked a little embarrassed and was obviously in some sort of predicament and had difficulty opening up about it.

"You are the only one who I trust to keep this to himself."

I suggested we should walk in the fields and talk there. I wondered what he was going to tell me. Before long, he started.

"When I returned from Italy, about ten years ago, I told the family about my time abroad, fighting for the Irish Brigade in the Papal Wars. But I didn't tell them the full story. Father, in particular, would be very upset if he heard all the gory details, especially as he didn't want me to go abroad in the first place."

There was a long pause and he continued.

"My problem is that I have dreadful nightmares about the terrible atrocities I saw in Italy. Mary obviously knows I have disturbed nights and I think she guesses the reason for my nightmares but we never talk about it. She is very supportive and watchful over me at night and wakes at the first sign of a disturbance and she quietens me down. So far, no one else in the family knows about this.

"I now know that I was not suited to military life. It was just a wonderful youthful ideal. I thought that by going to Italy we were going to change the world.

"I need to talk to someone about those times. It might help me get rid of the ghosts that stalk me at night. Can I share my story with you?"

I was upset to see my nephew in such a state but glad I might be able to help in some way. He was obviously suffering, his mood was low and he seemed depressed.

"Of course you can tell me if you think it will help, and I promise I won't tell anyone about this. I'm glad we've come outside. No one will hear us here."

Richard continued.

"In many ways, my journey was a great experience. I enjoyed seeing other countries and how other people live. Life in those countries is so different from here in our native Ireland. It also taught me how to live peacefully with my band of brothers.

"I went to Italy to fight for the Pope and for my religion. But it wasn't a bit like that. Like all wars, it had political undertones which the Pope and his lands had become embroiled in.

"After arriving in Italy, we had a long wait before going into battle. When it started, it was very harsh and I saw many of my compatriots killed. I told the family about being taken prisoner but I never told them the full details.

"I didn't tell them that after the battle, we were badly beaten in Ancona and shackled in irons. They sent us to prison in Genoa where the torture continued. The shackles were removed but our wrists and ankles were sore and bleeding. This attracted flies which were buzzing all around us so the wounds took a long time to heal.

"We were in prison for a long time – several weeks. There were 20 of us in one small cell. We lived on meagre rations and we shared our cell with rats and vermin. I can't explain to you how inhuman we humans can be, particularly when incarcerated together under such conditions. We'd been a proud band of brothers but in prison there were no brotherly feelings. With the exception of one or two, it was now each man for himself.

"In prison, we wore ragged clothes. These were the clothes we'd first worn when we travelled to Italy. We'd given our borrowed uniforms back to the Austrians. Our old clothes were filthy dirty and they'd never been washed. Water was scarce and we had no opportunity to wash ourselves or shave. We had all grown long beards and long hair.

"We had one bucket to relieve ourselves, used by all 20 of us. Sometimes the prison guards forgot to empty it and often it was full and overflowing. When they did come to get it, they said it was too heavy to carry and they tipped some of the contents out on the prison floor. The smell of the excrement was sickening and this attracted flies too. The lack of air worsened from day to day as the sun moved higher in the sky. We were baser than a pack of animals.

"At first, we had one meal a day which consisted of potatoes, some vegetables and if we were lucky a dash of gravy. If we asked for more, we were beaten. As time wore on, we often had days without food. Finally, we were given just a crust of bread a day. We all lost weight and shrank to skin and bones. The flesh fell away from our bodies. Our tattered clothes hung off us.

"We didn't see the light of day for many weeks. Our cell had one small window, about a foot square, positioned high on the outside wall. It was so high we couldn't see anything out of it except the blue sky. There was no glass in the opening so at least we had a little fresh air. In the hotter weather, it seemed as though we were in an oven and trapped forever. On those days, there was no air flow at all.

"When we were eventually released, my eyes were sore just looking at the daylight and I looked forward to night time when it grew dark. At first, I worried I was going blind. I realised that everyone else had the same problem. It took several days for us to become accustomed to the light again.

"I never wanted my mother, father or the rest of the family to know what terrible brutalities I endured. I didn't want them to know how badly we were treated. These are the atrocities which haunt me in my nightmares.

"Mary worries about me. I disturb her when I wake up, shouting and screaming. In my dreams, I am reliving those awful times. But I've never been able to tell her about them. I'm sure that sharing my troubles with you will help me. If so, I should rest better. Having unburdened myself, I already feel a great sense of relief. Thank you so much for listening. I feel better already."

I was surprised at the amount of degradation Richard had endured. He painted a very vivid picture of what had happened to him and I wasn't surprised that it had given him nightmares. But it was surprising how, talking about those times, helped him. Later, he told me he hadn't had a bad night for two weeks. He hoped he wouldn't have relapses but was prepared for this. He now knew the answer to his problem was to share his experiences with others. I told him if he had a recurrence, I would be happy to talk again.

I was glad that Richard seemed to have fought off his demons.

CHAPTER THIRTY-TWO

Richard was now firmly settled as the head teacher at Mohober School and, all being well, he could look forward to a good future. He was a dedicated teacher and all our children were under his care. One of the benefits of working for the Department of Education was that he received a regular salary. He was now the breadwinner of the family! This set our family on a stable footing. Richard's income was the mainstay of the family but the income from our farm had more than halved over recent years and the basket making had finished. Richard's salary was therefore very important to us.

Mohober School was just a short stroll from our house. The school building was once a small farmhouse and when the farmer and his family moved away, the building became vacant. The parish priest was keen to see a new national school in his neighbourhood so he notified the Department of Education that the building was empty and suitable for a school. The Department acted quickly and within a year it had set up Mohober National School.

Richard was happy with the old farm building which was plenty large enough for a school room. It was much bigger than our old workshop but, like many other buildings in Ireland, there was no running water or other facilities.

Children at Mohober paid a fee for their education. These payments were means tested so parents only paid as much as they could afford. There was one pupil who paid five shillings a quarter whilst some of the wealthiest paid more than £4, with the average payment about £2. We were fortunate that our children didn't have to pay.

Most of the children come from farming families. During the winter months, the average attendance is 80%. But during the summer months, it could drop to 30% or 40% as the children stayed at home on their farms to help with harvesting and other tasks. There was little Richard could do to force them back to school as their parents needed their help. The school inspector was never happy when he visited in summer and the attendance was low. He was not a country man and didn't understand the need for children to help out on their family farms.

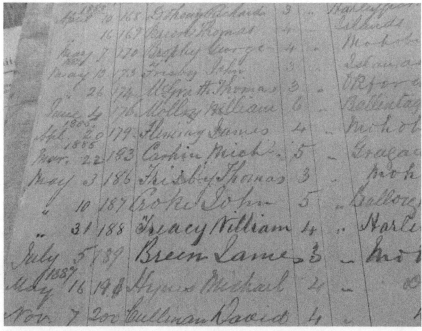

An excerpt from the Mohober School register containing the names of John Frisby and Thomas Frisby, who both started school at the age of three.

The school was well supplied with all its needs by the Department in Dublin.

Richard told me he had to stick to a set curriculum. He sometimes wandered from this and introduced other interesting topics. Since he had travelled abroad, he had a great interest in geography and his pupils were keen to hear about life in other lands.

Mohober Well was close to the school. It provided water for washing and drinking and was used by many people in the district. When the dry weather came and other wells and springs in the district dried up, Mohober Well kept running. At times of drought, people came from far and wide to fetch water. In the summer there were sometimes long queues for water and people carried it a long way back to their families. Some farmers even took barrel loads of water for their cattle.

The children brought their lunch to school. Some had bread and cheese but others had just a crust. After they'd eaten, they all ran to the Mohober Well for water. They cupped their hands together to catch the water and drank out of them.

There were several desks in the schoolroom. Richard's desk was taller than the others and was a bit like a preacher's rostrum. There was a small room adjacent to the large room, called the junk room. This was used for the children to hang up their outdoor clothes.

The children learned everything by repetition and there was never time to explain to them the rationale behind the figures. Learning by repetition had its benefits. One rarely forgot lessons learned by rote. As Richard was the only teacher at Mohober, he often found it difficult to cope with the different age groups. Fortunately, most children knew how lucky they were to be at school and they were keen to learn and caused little trouble. There was always a celebration when one of the young ones managed to write his or her name for the first time; a great cheer went up!

CHAPTER THIRTY-THREE

I must bring you up to date on family matters. The family continued to grow as Richard and Mary had children. By 1879 they had three lovely daughters: Catherine (Kate), Margaret (Maggie) and baby Bridget (Bridgie).

Bridgie was the youngest and was born in 1878. She brought them great joy and Kate and Maggie loved looking after her. Mary confided in me that she hoped their next baby would be a boy. Everyone hoped a new boy in the family would one day bring the farm back to its former glory.

Mother and Father would have been proud grandparents if they had been alive but they had both died in the same year, in 1867. If Mother had still been with us, I knew she would have been fussing over the girls, tying ribbons in their hair and making clothes for them.

¤

Richard was kept very busy with school. As well as teaching, he had to keep the account books, the roll books and the class lists. He spent a lot of time on the accounts which had to be in good order when the school inspector called.

Richard had always had a good relationship with the inspector but recently a new one was appointed who covered several schools in our locality. This man visited the school about once a year officially, but it was not unusual for him to make unexpected visits. On these occasions, he turned up unannounced. Richard worked out that his visits occurred about once a quarter. When he arrived, the inspector carefully checked all the accounts and the register, and any discrepancy would be reported to Dublin. Richard had to be careful not to slip up.

Richard had never had trouble with the inspector until now but he found the new man very awkward. After just one meeting, Richard came home and told me he thought he was too young for the job.

"He's full of advice. I think it all comes from text books. He's critical of the way I keep the account books but he found no errors in them. I wonder what I am doing wrong. All he does is criticise. I don't think he's ever been a teacher and he doesn't seem to understand my difficulties."

We could understand Richard's annoyance but I told him to give the new man a chance. He might be nervous in his new job. Richard laughed and said, "He was far from nervous. But, yes, let's see what happens next time."

One month later, the inspector appeared at the door unannounced. He was hardly through the door when he told Richard the Department had received a complaint against him from a parent who claimed that Richard had unjustly reprimanded his son. Richard recalled the incident which involved a boy creating havoc in the classroom. On the first occasion it happened, he sent the boy outside and told him to stay outside for half an hour. When the boy came back in, he warned him that if he continued to cause upset, he would be forced to use his cane. The next day, he started to cause a ruckus again and Richard took him outside and gave him a whack on his backside with his stick. Richard explained to the inspector that the boy had been wearing thick clothing and hadn't been hurt. But his pride was hurt in front of the other children and he ran home crying to his parents, saying Richard had harmed him.

The inspector said that the Department took complaints of this sort very seriously. They were looking into the matter and would decide whether or not to keep Richard on. Richard was furious but didn't show his feelings to the inspector. He just said he thought the punishment was justified.

The visit had upset Richard and after school he came home and told Mary how annoyed he was. She agreed the parent's complaint was unnecessary but she thought it was unlikely the Department would do anything.

It was several weeks before Richard heard the outcome of this unfortunate affair. Having looked into all the details, the Department of Education decided he had no case to answer. Richard was relieved but it had been a difficult few weeks while he waited for their decision. Unfortunately, this minor complaint remained on his record forever. Richard had rarely used his cane but decided he would never use it again, however much the children provoked him. It was a salutary lesson for him. If he had been found guilty of harming the boy, he could have been dismissed from his job.

When the decision was announced, the Department informed the boy's parents. They were annoyed and removed their boy from the school. Richard was sorry to see him go as he was a bright young lad with promise and he would have done well in the future but this would not be in Mohober School.

CHAPTER THIRTY-FOUR

There was great joy in the family in 1880 when, at last, Richard and Mary, had their first son. They called him John. He was a lovely little chap and was spoiled by his sisters, Kate, Maggie and Bridgie, who all took turns in looking after him.

Three years later, in 1883, Mary had another son named Thomas after our uncle who has gone to live in Carrick. Then, in 1885, little Patrick was born followed by Richard (yes, another Richard!) So they now had four sons and three daughters.

¤

The year 1879 was remembered for the great thunderstorm. The weather had been bad for months and we were plagued with rain and strong winds for many days.

Some of our older neighbours remembered the Year of the Big Wind but said this wasn't as bad as that had been. The storm did a lot of damage and resulted in a poor harvest for everyone. People who relied on their harvest to see them through the year were destitute and faced a year of hunger. We all stayed indoors as the lightning lit up the dark sky, rain poured down in torrents and thunder rumbled overhead. It was so bad that Richard closed the school for three days.

In Ballingarry, the storm stayed overhead for many days and people were terrified. Many of them went to the church to shelter and pray. Whilst sheltering, they heard loud claps of thunder and not long afterwards a big ball of lightning fell from above. People were so frightened they fled with fear into the sacristy. The lightning hit the belfry and split it in two. Fortunately, no one was hurt but it was a very frightening experience and was talked about for many days.

At Islands, whilst we sheltered indoors, we worried that our little river would overflow and flood the house. It was years since we had seen so much rain in such a short time. Fortunately, this time our little river didn't reach flood levels.

In spite of these occasional extreme weather events, the climate in our country is usually mild, moist and changeable. We have plenty of rainfall, some wind but we rarely have extreme temperatures. As a nation, we would always have a fascination with the weather.

Farmers like to predict the weather. They are guided by many events: when cows lie down in the field it means rain but a robin sitting high on the branch of a tree is a sign of good weather. Swallows flying high also bring good weather, but swallows flying low forecast rain, and so on and so on. Jack has always been the weather watcher in the family and he looks to the sun, moon, stars, sky and clouds for signals.

Our wheat crop was battered by the storm that year. It had not grown to its full height and now lay flattened on the ground. Thankfully, we had a good store of oats and flour to fall back on, thanks to careful planning, so we wouldn't starve. It wouldn't be long before we killed the pig again. It had been a hard year but we were managing to get by.

Jack didn't give up after the storm. As soon as the useless wheat crop was removed from the field, he set about tilling the earth again ready for the next year. He walked the fields every evening, praying that next year would be better. Normally, when times were good, he walked the fields at the end of every day, making sure that all was in order and blessing the crops. Now there was no crop for him to bless.

The storm was talked about for days. Thankfully, after three or four weeks we seemed to have dried out and hopefully we wouldn't have to go through this ordeal again for a few years.

CHAPTER THIRTY-FIVE

Our landlord's agent called twice a year, at the end of March and the end of September, to collect the rent. He was a pleasant man and always stopped with us for a drink while we talked about the state of the world. But he never inspected the house or the land and seemed to be happy to continue as before. I hoped this continued for many years. It would be wonderful to see yet another generation of Frisbys living in the house.

Richard and Mary's children give us great pleasure. We loved having them around the house. If the weather was fine, they'd go out and play in the field at the back of the house. It was not unusual to hear their screams and shouts as they enjoyed themselves. One day, Catherine came running in and said to Mary,

"Look what I've found! A four-leaf clover! Will it bring us all good luck?"

In the evenings, at about eight o'clock, we gathered together in the kitchen around the fireside where Mary would tell the children folk tales. These stories had been told in the family down the ages and were about the faeries, the wee folk, and the leprechauns. The boys liked to hear tales about the rainbow and searches for pots of gold. They dreamt of one day finding the end of the rainbow themselves.

One night, one of Richard's boys said to his mother, "Ma, tell us another story."

Mary hesitated and said, "Have I told you the one about the changeling?"

"No!" the children chorused.

They all sat round enraptured as she told them about Mrs. Flattery who took her daughter to the lake one day to catch fish. When the mother's back was turned, the little girl was whisked away by the faeries and a changeling was put in her place. Mrs. Flattery didn't see this incident and had no reason to think anything had happened. She went home with her daughter and it was when she was preparing tea that she noticed that the girl was cutting up the table cloth with a pair of scissors. She scolded her. This wasn't like her daughter. Time went on and the little girl got naughtier and naughtier. The father, Mr. Flattery, was exasperated by the things that were happening. "She's not ours," he said. "She's a changeling – when did this bad behaviour start?"

Mrs Flattery thought about it and said it had been happening since they went to the lake.

"That's it! Have you not heard tales of the bad faeries at the lake? You should never have taken her there. We must take her back and find our real daughter."

They set out that evening and reached the lake at sunset. All was quiet. The priest and some of their neighbours had come with them for protection against the evil spirits. The priest held the changeling up in his arms and walked into the lake. He said, "The only way to get your daughter back is to put this one into the water."

A sigh went up from the watching crowd, which by now had grown to several hundred. They didn't want to see the changeling drowned. At that moment a cry came from the woods.

"Wait, don't do that!" They all looked in the direction of this noise and saw a little girl coming out of the woods.

"It's our Brenda!" said Mr. Flattery. "The faeries have sent her back to us."

The crowd was hushed as Brenda ran towards her parents. They were re-united and no one saw the changeling again. She had vanished into thin air. A cheer went up from the crowd and everyone made their way home.

"The moral of the story," Mary said, "is don't take your daughter to the lake. You might lose her."

There was silence in the room when Mary finished. The children had not heard about changelings before but they were all glad that the story had a happy ending. Folk stories like this were told all over the country.

When they were old enough, Mary taught the children to say their rosary prayers, an important part of family life in all Catholic homes in Ireland.

Mary started by reciting the trimmings of the rosary and, as the children grew older, they were encouraged to contribute to the prayers. Now that we didn't have to be up so early in the morning for the farm, we didn't go to bed as early and our evenings were longer. Even so, we were usually all in bed by ten o'clock. We all slept well and were all up and about by seven o'clock in the morning.

¤

School didn't start until nine o'clock and Richard had time after breakfast to prepare lessons for the day. He left home at eight o'clock and got the school room ready for the day ahead. Children would start to arrive at about quarter to nine and he enjoyed listening to their chatter. He heard all the neighbourhood gossip from them and we were all amused when he related these tales to us in the evening.

Richard had appointed a monitor to help him at school. He came in early and distributed the wooden frames the children used for counting. The frames contained coloured beads rather like an abacus. He also distributed the slates and chalk used by the younger children.

The older children learned to write on paper and the monitor distributed ink and pens, which were fashioned from sticks with steel needles. The pens ran dry quickly and had to be dipped into ink every few words. They were not very satisfactory but they were the only pens available.

Once a week, they had a singing lesson. Richard was not a singer and found the lesson difficult. However, it was important for the children to learn hymns and the national anthem. Some families in our area didn't like their children singing the British anthem so when Richard received complaints, he had to explain that we were still part of the British Empire and we had to abide by the rules set by the Department of Education. Things like this went against the grain as most people were still striving for an independent Ireland. Some parents complained about the picture of Queen Victoria in the schoolroom and the Union Jack on the wall.

Not many people were aware that schools had an ode of loyalty to Queen Victoria of England but it appeared in the second primer:

"God bless our native land
May heaven's protecting hand
Still guard our shores
Through every changing scene
O, Lord, preserve the Queen,
Long may she reign!"

When Richard first saw this, he shuddered. He knew many parents would object to it. Fortunately, very few of them were aware of its existence so it wasn't a problem. Some parents had very entrenched views and thought the children should be taught the Irish language but Richard was not allowed to do this.

History was also taught in school via a history book supplied by the Department – the lessons were all about British history and Richard was not allowed to teach Irish history. He, like many others, found this strange. But Irish history was kept alive by the folk tales told in most families. Maybe, in times to come, teaching Irish history would be allowed.

Richard had recently appointed a lady at school to give the girls sewing lessons. Girls learned to sew at home from an early age, but only in a rudimentary way. Catholic families tended to be large and most children wore clothes handed down from their elder siblings, which had to be adjusted to fit the next wearer. The girls had to do this themselves if their mother was busy. Some girls came to school in ill-fitting clothing which they had clearly worked on themselves and the results were not always good.

Elaine Cody was a professional dressmaker and charged a small fee for her services which was approved by the Department. She knew the girls had a basic understanding of needlework so she taught them the finer points of sewing and dressmaking. The girls enjoyed these lessons.

¤

Richard's wife Mary was now in charge of all household duties. Jack's wife, Catherine, ran the home for many years. It was a great relief to her when Richard was married and his wife Mary moved in with us as Catherine was able to take a back seat.

To everyone's surprise, in 1888 Mary was pregnant again. Richard and Mary would have eight children! I often wondered how we managed to feed all those mouths. But we were more fortunate than most families. Richard's income paid the rent and bought any extra items we needed.

The most expensive item we had to buy was shoes. Imagine how much it cost to buy these for all the adults and children in the family! We saw many children from large families going to school barefoot. No one likes inheriting someone else's footwear so it was rarely handed down in families but poor families didn't have enough money to buy shoes for everyone. For many years, we managed to ensure that all the children were properly shod. We repaired the shoes ourselves and the boys knocked hob nails into the soles to make them last longer.

¤

Mary gave birth to her last daughter and called her Mary Ann. This was soon shortened to Marian and she was the darling of the family and loved by all. Maggie and Kate enjoyed taking care of their new young sister. Bridget, on the other hand, prefered to be outdoors playing with her brothers and the neighbours' boys. She was growing into a tomboy.

¤

Life was to be interrupted again. My brother Jack, or Granpa Jack as he was called by the children, gave up farming. One day he fell ill and didn't rise from his bed. We all worried about him. I talked to him a lot in those days while he lay in bed. I was sad to see my brother laid so low. He had once been so active. He knew he was not going to live long and we prayed for him. He passed away peacefully one night in 1892 and the whole family was distressed at his passing. As one of the children said, "He's always been here. It'll be so strange now without him."

¤

Thomas was the brightest child in our family. He took to learning quickly and there wasn't much more he could learn at Mohober. In 1895, when Tom was 12 years old, Richard entered him in the entrance exam for the school run by the De la Salle Brothers in Waterford. We were delighted when he passed the exam and gained a scholarship. There would be no school fees to pay but we'd have to provide items such as school uniform and other equipment.

Tom would be a boarder at the school so Richard was worried about the logistics of getting him back and forth. He realised it would be difficult and we had no idea how we were going to manage this.

Waterford is about 40 to 50 miles away and no public coach went from our district to Waterford. When Richard took him there for the exam, they went by donkey and cart and stayed overnight at an inn before returning home. Poor old Ned was getting old and we didn't think he could manage that journey again. Donkeys are great workhorses but using him like this, at his age, was a risk. The Bianconi coaches and the mail coaches didn't go our way so we were stumped. We were trying to find another way of getting him there. We made enquiries to see if anyone locally travelled there and if so, maybe we could hitch a lift.

Richard went to see the priest who was the font of all knowledge. He didn't know anyone going there but he said he would ask around. However, we heard no more from him.

I decided to visit David Frisby in Ballyduggan. He was delighted to hear the news of Tom's success in the exam. I told him about our worries and said we thought poor old Ned might not make the journey.

David didn't know of anyone who travelled to Waterford but he lost no time in offering to lend us his pony and trap.

"You'll have to spend at least one night away from home, maybe two nights."

I was delighted and said I would take good care of it.

I drove home in David's trap, with Ned and our cart tied up behind. The family all came out to see me as I drove up the laneway towards Islands. You'd think they had never seen a pony and trap before! It was a novelty for them. The pony was called Sonny and we had to take great care of her. She was soon stabled in our barn and the children made sure she had oats to eat and plenty of hay and water.

I offered to take Tom to school as Richard was busy at school. The day of our departure soon arrived. Richard and Mary made sure Tom had all he needed. He had just turned 13 years old and was looking grand in his new school uniform which they had bought in Kilkenny. He had a small case for his belongings and we put this in the back of the trap before we set off. We left very early in the morning and the family waved us goodbye. I had studied the road maps the previous day so I was confident we would get there safely. The journey was a long one and it took us several hours to get there. When we reached the town, we had to ask directions to the school.

When we arrived at the school, Tom was eager to go inside and would have been happy if I had left him on the doorstep. But I insisted on taking him in. It was obvious he didn't want me hanging around so I made a fairly quick exit, telling him to remember to write to us.

"We'll all want to know how you're getting on," I said. "Good luck in everything you do."

As I left the school, I waved goodbye to Tom. I then had to decide whether to journey home or find somewhere to stay for the night. The family wouldn't be expecting me home that night and I was tired at the thought of the long journey, and it would soon be getting dark. I was concerned that I might lose my way in the dark and I decided to call on the Frisby family near Mullinavat in southern Kilkenny. I hoped they would offer me a bed for the night but if they didn't, I could stay at an inn in one of the nearby villages.

I arrived at Red Acres as the sun was setting behind their farmhouse. I tethered the pony and went to knock on their door. Michael Frisby had seen me coming and opened the door, saying, "Welcome!" as he stepped out to meet me. "What brings you here?" I told him the reason for my visit. He introduced me to his wife Johanna and my luck was in as, when she heard I had nowhere to stay, she offered me a bed for the night which I gladly accepted.

It had been a long day and even though I was tired, I was glad to sit down at the supper table and join the family for the evening meal. I had first met Michael's father, James, when he travelled up for David Frisby's wedding many years ago. In the intervening years, we had kept in touch only rarely. Now I was meeting all of Michael's large family. They were a good crowd but I thought, *I'll never remember all these names.*

During the evening meal, I told them I had taken Tom to school in Waterford and they wanted to know all about this and were keen for news of the family. I couldn't have had a better reception. As our families didn't meet often, we had a lot to catch up on. We were related in some way, but it was so far back we didn't know our exact relationship and we only met on rare occasions, usually at weddings or funerals.

We had a grand family dinner with everyone asking me different questions. They were impressed at Tom's success in his exam. When they realised what a long journey we'd had, they suggested Tom should stay with them for the half-term holiday to save me travelling down again in just a few weeks. I was grateful for this and thanked them. I wouldn't have to do the journey again until the end of term. I thought it would be good for Tom to get to know his distant cousins and I hoped Richard and Mary would agree.

Over supper, I told them all about David Frisby and his family and news about the Killamery Frisbys. They had seen in the newspaper that William Frisby from Killamery had appeared in court and they wanted to know all about this. I told them about the incident which occurred in the Killamery pub. William Frisby ran the pub called *The Auld House*, situated on the main road at Killamery between Callan and Carrick-on-Suir.

The court case was brought against them because they'd opened the pub on Christmas Day. A member of the Garda had called in when they were serving drinks and reported them. They were reprimanded at a court appearance but no fine was payable. They were warned not to let it happen again. Everyone laughed at the story and they were glad it wasn't anything more serious.

I told them that William was frequently up in court for some small misdemeanours, such as letting his sheep wander and graze on his neighbour's pasture. David Frisby had also been in court for a similar charge. These two families made many court appearances over the years. They were always in trouble, one way or another. These were only petty offences and were not malicious.

In turn, they gave me news of the Frisby families living near them in Smithstown and neighbouring districts. The family was huge and I knew I would never remember everything they told me.

The following day, I returned home with much news to tell the family. I had written down the names of the children so I was able to tell them these. Like me, they had difficulty remembering the names of this big family. After my visit to Waterford, life soon returned to normal.

¤

Mother had been like a lost soul since Father died and it was not long before she followed him, in 1896. In the three or four years since he had passed, she had been very quiet and not like her usual cheerful self. This was the end of that generation. We buried her in the family grave at Modeshill and arranged for a large marble Celtic cross with their names engraved on it. The grave was surrounded by iron railings and stood proudly looking in the direction of Slievenamon.

¤

We would soon be entering a new millennium. Times were changing fast and chances of employment for our children would be difficult, as they had always been. I often wondered what they would all do. We had given them a good start in life but it would soon be up to them to make their way in a difficult world. I hoped one of them would follow in the family tradition of teaching. This might be Tom when he finished school in Waterford. Perhaps one of our boys would take to farming and restore our farm to its former glory. At the moment, they were all too young to know what the future held for them, but they were all growing up quickly and soon decisions would have to be made. Time would fly by quickly.

I was surprised at how quickly events were enfolding. Not long after Tom started at his new school, his sister Kate, Richard's eldest daughter, announced she would be marrying her boyfriend, John Cleary. This pleased us. We liked John and he had a respectful job with the constabulary, recently promoted to constable. Our only concern was the difference in their ages: Kate was 17 years old and John was 28 – more than ten years older than her. This seemed a big gap but they were very fond of each other and both sensible people. There was a possibility that John Cleary might be sent to work in another county which often happened in the constabulary. They didn't like their men working in the counties where their families lived. John assured us this wouldn't happen immediately and could be several months or possibly years away. We hoped for the latter. If they moved away, we would miss them.

Kate had a lovely wedding, with her sisters acting as flower girls. She went to live with John at his parents' home near Windgap, about three miles east of Mullinahone. Mary missed Kate when she had gone. She had been such a help in the house. Maggie tried to take her place in the kitchen but she was slow and clumsy and Mary found her more of a hindrance than a help. I sometimes wondered if Maggie was deliberately clumsy to get out of work.

Bridgie, on the other hand, was proving a great help to Richard and he had appointed her as a monitor at school. She looked after the younger children for him while he concentrated on the older pupils.

¤

The talk in the neighbourhood now was all about emigration. Parents saw a better future for their children abroad. Many of our neighbours' children had emigrated and three of my cousin George Frisby's children had emigrated to Australia. That seemed to be a long way to go. I talked to Richard about this. He hoped his children wouldn't leave Ireland, but if they did, he would prefer them to go to America as it was not such a long journey. Many young people from Ballingarry had gone to America where they said, "the streets are paved with gold" – but I doubted it.

Mary gave Richard her sister's address in New York.

"Write to Eileen, Richard," she said. "As you know, she runs a small dressmaking business and I'm sure she would be glad to take the girls on. If they have to go, I would be happy if they are settled with her."

Two boys of the Carey family, who lived just down our laneway, had gone to America in the last two years. Our children had been hearing news of them from their mother and Patrick went to see Mrs. Carey yesterday and came home to tell us how they were getting on.

Mrs. Carey said to him, "Don't you believe it now, when people tell you that the streets of New York are paved with gold. There's no such thing. Life is hard there." She went on to tell Pat that her boys were managing to get by, but life had not been easy for them.

"Everyone who goes to America has to declare to the shipping company details of the person they are going to live with. They also have to show they have enough money with them to see them through the first few months. Unfortunately, the uncle they named on their travel documents had moved away and no one was there to meet them from the ship. They had to find their own way round. At first, they had a terrible time. They were befriended at the dockside in New York by an Irishman and he told them where to find somewhere to live. They were tired and weary and eventually arrived at a run-down tenement block on the lower-east side of Manhattan. They moved into one room which they shared with two other Irishmen." Gary wrote home and told his mother about their experiences and in his letter he said, 'I don't want to worry you, mother, but we could have done better by moving to Dublin's slums.'

Mrs. Carey said to Pat, "Don't believe all you hear about The American Dream."

There were many tenement blocks in New York which housed thousands of immigrants from many European countries. The Carey boys were fortunate as they had found their way to the area where most Irish immigrants lived. Although not completely comfortable with their surroundings, they were amongst their own countrymen. But it was far from satisfactory. These tenements were old, run-down, over-crowded and lacked amenities such as running water and there was a lot of illness.

"If I had known what they were going to," Mrs. Carey said, "I wouldn't have let them go. After I received Gary's letter, I had many sleepless nights worrying about them. My poor boys. They left a good, clean Irish home and they ended up in a real mess. Thank goodness only two of them have gone. My two younger boys want to go too. I'm telling them there is no way I will let them out of my sight."

Patrick came home and gave us this news. Richard had taught the Carey boys at school and said, "Those two boys have good heads on them. If anyone can survive, they will." That evening Richard and Mary talked again about emigration for their children. Richard said the only way he would let any of their children go would be if they were met by relatives and had a job sorted out and somewhere to live before they sailed. Mary agreed and reminded him he was going to write to her sister in New York.

A few months later, Patrick visited Mrs. Carey again and she said to him, "I have better news at last. Gary and Neil both have jobs and will soon be sending money home! At first, they were despondent as the only jobs they could find were on the roads, the canals or the railways. These jobs are well paid but they didn't want to become navvies. Then they discovered that many jobs were vacant in hotels in uptown New York. They are now working in a grand hotel as bartenders and they have been given smart uniforms and they both live there."

Patrick was enthused by what he had heard and said he wanted to go abroad and make a living there. Richard and Mary were worried about him. He was far too young to leave school and wander off abroad. He hadn't thought it through and he was likely to act before he thought about the consequences. Richard had forbidden him to go and they were now not talking to one another. I couldn't help thinking 'like father, like son!' as I remembered Richard himself being forbidden to go overseas by his father. History was repeating itself!

John and Richard also expressed an interest in going to New York. They were far too young to be thinking of this yet as they still had more years at school. Richard and Mary were concerned about them. It looked as if Thomas would be the only son to find work in Ireland. Even though he might have to move away from Islands, at least he'd still be in Ireland. Richard had always hoped that the education he had given his children would enable them to find work in Ireland but as the years went by, this looked less and less likely and he had sadly come to the conclusion that eventually he would have to give in to them and let them go. He had now written to Mary's sister in New York to see if she could offer anything for Bridgie and

Maggie but so far he hadn't had a reply. Most girls in the area seemed to be getting married and settling down to have families but Bridgie and Maggie had not shown any inclination to do this. They had a few boyfriends but nothing serious.

We had been a close-knit family for many years, with people rarely moving away. It now increasingly looked as if that trend would be broken. We couldn't imagine what poor old Islands would be like without the voices of young children about the place! The future was uncertain. The new millennium loomed ahead of us and things would be very different.

There had always been a tradition of the young looking after the older people in the family and it had always worked well. I couldn't remember a time when there hadn't been three generations of the family living under our roof. But now it looked as if our children would leave home which was so far from what we had hoped for them. We always thought that one of the boys would work on the farm and bring it back to its former glory but it was beginning to look as if emigration was the only hope. Hopefully, if they did go, they would be able to build their lives in America.

Then a letter arrived from Mary's sister in New York. Richard took the letter into the parlour and sat quietly to read it to himself. When he had finished, he folded it up and put it in his top pocket. He was pleased with the contents but thought it was too soon to share it with the family. Mary had seen the letter arrive so he would read it to her later, when the family were not around.

That evening, before the family congregated for their supper, Richard told Mary about the letter he had received from her sister and he read it to her.

Dear Richard,

Thank you for your letter. I was pleased to hear from you and to read all your news. I'm glad you have survived all the horrors that this century has brought to our dear old Ireland.

We are well here and the business is good. My problem is that I can't find the staff. Young girls come and go as it pleases them. It is difficult to find girls who want a permanent job or who have done any needlework. So, we have to start right at the beginning with them and show them the basics – even teaching them how to thread a needle! So, I am always looking for good girls to work in my dressmaking business and I would be delighted to give Bridget and Maggie jobs and a home if they decide to come to New York. I know this will take much time to organise and I don't expect you will make a quick decision. But the offer is there and I hope that in due course you will be able to take it up.

As for the boys, well, I can't offer them jobs or a home but I have lots of Irish emigree friends who may be able to help. I will ask around and let you know if I find anything.

In the meantime, I encourage you to make enquiries about emigration. In due course you will have to find out about ships, their timings and other things like passports. I leave it in your capable hands.

Finally, please be assured that Bridget and Maggie would receive a warm welcome here if they come. I look forward to hearing further from you.

Please give my love to my sister Mary. Oh, what I would give to see her and the family again! Tell her there are some Corcorans here – but they are not ours!

My love to you all, Eileen.

Mary was so glad to hear from her sister and reading her letter brought tears to her eyes. They hadn't been in touch for several years. Now they had this offer, neither she nor Richard could bear to contemplate losing their girls. The letter brought home to them the finality of allowing them to go. They decided to say nothing about it to Bridget and Maggie.

Richard said, "I'm sure the offer will still be there even in a couple of years' time. So, let's forget about it for a while. We don't need to make an immediate decision."

"I agree, Richard," Mary replied. "Let's sleep on it. In a few months we might feel quite differently. I'm really glad to hear from

Eileen. She's doing so well and there are clearly opportunities in New York."

¤

Time flew by and suddenly it is 1897. Richard will soon be retiring as teacher at Mohober School where he has worked for over 30 years. Our book has covered a period of 100 years of family life. We have managed to survive through some very troubled times in our country and have been very lucky. I believe that our struggles for independence from the British will continue. People are becoming more enlightened and I hope that these struggles will not have been in vain. I can see a time in the future when Ireland will be a Free State and I hope this will not be far away.

With Richard's retirement approaching fast and with thoughts of children leaving home, I have decided to bring this book to an end and so I say goodbye to you. If you would like to know more about what happened to the Frisby family, you can read about them in *First To Go - The True Story of Bridget Frisby*.

I leave you with the thought that this book would not have been written without our hedge schools!

THE END

EPILOGUE

As I was writing *Penalised*, I heard stories of the Taliban in Afghanistan and their refusal to educate women and girls. What a long way we have come since the early 19th century, and how far back has Afghanistan travelled in just a few years! How many years will it be before all girls and women throughout the world are treated as equal with men?

Penalised is a prequel to *First to Go* (or *The True Story of Bridget Frisby*), but written after *First to Go*, where you can read more about what happened to the family after 1900.

Both books are rich and compelling historical novels, rigorously researched, which depict Ireland in the 19th century. From Ireland to America and Europe, each backdrop and event is finely detailed and provides a wealth of social history.

BIBLIOGRAPHY/SOURCES

BOOKS
History and Antiquities of the Diocese of Ossory, William Carrigan
Callan 800 Years – History & Heritage, Callan Heritage Society 2007
Coolagh – History & Heritage, Coolagh Centenary Committee 1996
The Great Shame, Thomas Keneally
The Big Sycamore, Joseph Brady
Knocknagow – Homes of Tipperary, Charles J Kickham
Ballingarry Parish Journal
Callan Tenant Protection Society (1849), Callan Heritage Society
Book of Survey & Distribution, National Library of Ireland
A Topographical Dictionary of Ireland 1837, S. Lewis

INTERNET
Ancestry.com, a genealogy site
Wikipedia
The Schools' Collection of Memories, County Tipperary
The National Library of Ireland, Dublin
The National Archives of Ireland, Dublin

GENERAL
I have drawn on many family recollections from uncles and aunts, all
of which have been incorporated in *Penalised* and *First to Go*.

ACKNOWLEDGMENTS

I am forever indebted to my late aunt Esme (RIP) and my late uncle Leslie (RIP) for the many family stories they told me about the Frisby family in Ireland. I travelled with Esme to Ireland in 1991 and we found the house in Islands where our family had lived.

The house at Islands in about 1905 with, from left to right, John J Cleary, Richard Frisby, Bab-Ann Cleary, Mary Frisby and Mary Ann Frisby.

We visited the parish priest, Father Philip Morris (RIP), who kindly showed us church records for the Frisby family. (Records were not online in 1991). From these details we constructed our Frisby Family Tree.

Three generations of the family are buried in the family grave at Modeshill. Frisbys from other times were also buried in this cemetery but, with the ravages of time, all traces of their graves have disappeared.

The Frisby family gravestone faces Slievenamon in the distance. This photo of the family grave was taken in 1991. Sadly, the headstone has since fallen and broken, and needs replacing. The grave is encircled with iron railings.

My thanks go to the staff at the National Archives in Dublin who have always been helpful. Thanks also go to the staff at the National Library in Dublin.

I must thank my friend, Olga Belding, who has done sterling work in editing my manuscript. A distant cousin in Ireland read it too and made many observations of her own on life in Ireland in the 20th century. I am grateful to her for her helpful guidance. Also, my thanks go to my friend, Anne Chidgey, who has made useful suggestions. Thank you all for your differing contributions.

Finally, thanks to my family for letting me spend hours researching and writing *Penalised* and *First to Go*. In particular, my thanks go to my long-suffering husband, Michael. Thank you, Mike, for all the cups of tea and coffee which kept me going.

ABOUT THE AUTHOR

Pam was born in Cardiff but spent most of her early life in Bristol where she was educated at the Red Maids School. After leaving school she did not follow any usual career path but after a short spell at a commercial college she took a secretarial job and later managed to achieve success in business in London as firstly an Export Manager then as a Company Director. The rest of her working life was spent in business back in Bristol with her husband Michael. Pam and Michael have one son, David. On her retirement Pam took up various hobbies – golf, genealogy, travel and bridge. Her love of genealogy led her to discover much about her family, on which this novel is based.

Printed in Great Britain
by Amazon